EACHER GUIDE

Includes Stu...
Workshe...

Grammar

Answer Key

4th–6th Grade

Elementary Bible and English Grammar

MASTER BOOKS
— CURRICULUM —

First printing: September 2016
Fourth printing: September 2018

Copyright © 2014 by Master Books®. All rights reserved. No part of this book may be used or reproduced in any manner whatsoever without written permission of the publisher, except in the case of brief quotations in articles and reviews.
For information write:

Master Books®, P.O. Box 726, Green Forest, AR 72638

Master Books® is a division of the New Leaf Publishing Group, Inc.

ISBN: 978-1-68344-005-5
ISBN: 978-1-61458-579-4 (digital)

Unless otherwise noted, Scripture quotations are from the New King James Version of the Bible.

Printed in the United States of America

Please visit our website for other great titles:
www.masterbooks.com

For information regarding author interviews,

please contact the publicity department at (870) 438-5288.

Permission is granted for copies of reproducible pages from this text to be made for use within your own homeschooling family activities. Material may not be posted online, distributed digitally, or made available as a download. Permission for any other use of the material must be requested prior to use by email to the publisher at info@nlpg.com.

I'm loving this whole line so much. It's changed our homeschool for the better!

—Amy ★★★★★

Your reputation as a publisher is stellar. It is a blessing knowing anything I purchase from you is going to be worth every penny!

—Cheri ★★★★★

Last year we found Master Books and it has made a HUGE difference.

—Melanie ★★★★★

We love Master Books and the way it's set up for easy planning!

—Melissa ★★★★★

You have done a great job. MASTER BOOKS ROCKS!

—Stephanie ★★★★★

Physically high-quality, Biblically faithful, and well-written.

—Danika ★★★★★

Best books ever. Their illustrations are captivating and content amazing!

—Kathy ★★★★★

Affordable
Flexible
Faith Building

MASTERBOOKS
—CURRICULUM—

Table of Contents

We live in a visually oriented society where people learn from a blend of both text and images. The collection of events and teachings from Scripture in the Illustrated Family Bible Stories explores selected chapters and verses, and provides additional highlights into more than 200 Biblical accounts, psalms, proverbs, prophecies, laws, and letters, as well as the daily life of people living in the Old and New Testament times. With the help of maps, photographs, and diagrams, the ancient cultures of the Bible are set in a context that can be readily understood. In addition, specially written teaching helps to educate today's young reader in understanding the Bible's meaning and its relevance for everyday life.

Using This Teacher Guide

Features: The suggested weekly schedule enclosed has easy-to-manage lessons that guide the reading, worksheets, and all assessments. The pages of this guide are perforated and three-hole punched so materials are easy to tear out, hand out, grade, and store. Teachers are encouraged to adjust the schedule and materials needed in order to best work within their unique educational program.

Lesson Scheduling: Students are instructed to read the pages in their book and then complete the corresponding section provided by the teacher. Assessments that may include worksheets, activities, quizzes, and tests are given at regular intervals with space to record each grade. Space is provided on the weekly schedule for assignment dates, and flexibility in scheduling is encouraged. Teachers may adapt the scheduled days per each unique student situation. As the student completes each assignment, this can be marked with an "X" in the box.

	Approximately 30 to 45 minutes per lesson, five days a week
	Includes answer keys for worksheets, quizzes, and tests
	Worksheets for every lesson
	Quizzes and tests are included to help reinforce learning and provide assessment opportunities
	Designed for grades 4 to 6 in a one-year course

Course Objectives: Students completing this course will:

- Investigate the ancient cultures of the Bible as they learn grammatical principles
- Become familiar with words and their definitions, expanding their vocabulary
- Identify verses of Scripture through memory verses and Bible instruction
- Learn through hands-on activities that are both fun and educational
- Study English and Bible together, to help inspire their minds as well as their hearts.

Course Description

Help Bible history come alive for children so they know these true events that changed the world forever, at the same time they are developing their reading skills. We live in a visually oriented society where people learn from a blend of both text and images. This collection of events and teachings from Scripture explores selected chapters and verses. With the help of maps, photographs, and diagrams, the ancient cultures of the Bible are set in a context that can be readily understood. In addition, specially written teaching helps to educate today's young reader in understanding the Bible's meaning and its relevance for everyday life.

We encourage parental involvement, particularly with more mature or difficult biblical concepts, such as salvation. We instruct students to discuss such topics with a parent. The memory verse should be introduced on Monday. The student should have it memorized and recite it to a parent by Friday. The New International Version (NIV) is used for the memory verse, but students may use any version of the Bible.

Vocabulary word definitions may vary but should match the context of the words in the text. Students may begin worksheets at the beginning of the week and complete them as they read the text. Parents may use their discretion with the order of completion. Activities are a hands-on, fun way to learn the material. They are optional but highly recommended. Some activities may take longer than one day to complete. Parents may want to assign a due date to such activities.

Quizzes: Quizzes are optional and should be assigned at the parent's discretion. The maturity of the student should determine whether the quizzes are open book.

Additional materials: It is highly recommended that student have a Bible with a concordance and other helps in the version of the parent's choice. Students will also need several stacks of note cards and miscellaneous materials for the activities.

Grading Options for This Course

It is always the prerogative of a parent/educator to assess student grades however he or she might deem best. The following is only a suggested guideline based on the material presented through this course:

To calculate the percentage of the worksheets, quizzes, and tests, the parent/educator may use the following guide. Divide total number of questions correct (example: 43) by the total number of questions possible (example: 46) to calculate the percentage out of 100 possible. 43/46 = 93 percent correct.

The suggested grade values are noted as follows: 90 to 100 percent = A; 80 to 89 percent = B; 70 to 79 percent = C; 60 to 69 percent = D; and 0 to 59 percent = F.

First Semester Suggested Daily Schedule

Date	Day	Assignment	Due Date	✓	Grade
		First Semester-First Quarter			
Week 1	Day 1	Read Pages 8-9 • Introduction to the Bible *Illustrated Family Bible Stories* • (IFBS)			
	Day 2	Read Pages 12-13 • The Old Testament • (IFBS)			
	Day 3	Read Pages 14-15 • God makes the world • (IFBS)			
	Day 4	Read Page 16 • Sin spoils the creation • (IFBS)			
	Day 5	Weekly Worksheet 1 • Pages 15-16 • *Teacher Guide Lesson Planner* • (LP)			
Week 2	Day 6	Read Page 17 • Cain murders Abel • (IFBS)			
	Day 7	Read Pages 18-19 • Noah builds the great ark • (IFBS)			
	Day 8	Read Page 20 • Babbling tongues • (IFBS)			
	Day 9	Read Page 21 • God calls Abraham • (IFBS)			
	Day 10	Weekly Worksheet 2 • Pages 17-18 • (LP)			
Week 3	Day 11	Read Pages 22-23 • God's chosen people • (IFBS)			
	Day 12	Read Page 24 • Longing for a son • (IFBS)			
	Day 13	Read Page 25 • Ishmael is born to a servant • (IFBS)			
	Day 14	Read Pages 26-27 • The city of Sodom / Lot and his wife • (IFBS)			
	Day 15	Weekly Worksheet 3 • Pages 19-20 • (LP)			
Week 4	Day 16	Read Page 28 • Isaac's birth brings great joy • (IFBS)			
	Day 17	Read Page 29 • Sacrifice your son • (IFBS)			
	Day 18	Read Pages 30-31 • A beautiful bride for Isaac / Jacob takes Esau's blessing • (IFBS)			
	Day 19	Read Pages 32-33 • Jacob works long and hard / Welcome home, brother • (IFBS)			
	Day 20	Weekly Worksheet 4 • Pages 21-23 • (LP)			
Week 5	Day 21	Read Page 34 • Joseph's dreams • (IFBS)			
	Day 22	Read Pages 35-36 • Joseph sold as a slave / Thrown into prison • (IFBS)			
	Day 23	Read Pages 37-38 • Tell me what my dreams mean / Joseph put in charge • (IFBS)			
	Day 24	Read Page 39 • Joseph feeds his family • (IFBS)			
	Day 25	Weekly Worksheet 5 • Pages 25-26 • (LP)			
Week 6	Day 26	Read Pages 40-41 • A baby in the reeds / Moses stands on holy ground • (IFBS)			
	Day 27	Read Pages 42-43 • Plagues strike Egypt / Death passes over God's people • (IFBS)			
	Day 28	Read Pages 44-45 • The journey to the Promised Land • (IFBS)			
	Day 29	Read Pages 46-47 • Crossing the Red Sea / God feeds His people • (IFBS)			
	Day 30	Weekly Worksheet 6 • Pages 27-28 • (LP)			

Date	Day	Assignment	Due Date	✓	Grade
Week 7	Day 31	Read Pages 48-49 • The Ten Commandments / God's holy laws (IFBS)			
	Day 32	Read Pages 50-51 • The golden calf angers God • (IFBS)			
	Day 33	Read Pages 52-53 • We will not enter Canaan! / The bronze snake • (IFBS)			
	Day 34	Read Page 54 • The donkey that spoke • (IFBS)			
	Day 35	Weekly Worksheet 7 • Pages 29-30 • (LP)			
Week 8	Day 36	Read Pages 55-56 • A new leader is chosen / Send in the spies (IFBS)			
	Day 37	Read Pages 57-58 • The river stops flowing / The walls fall down (IFBS)			
	Day 38	Read Page 59 • Disaster at Ai • (IFBS)			
	Day 39	Read Page 60 • Making a home • (IFBS)			
	Day 40	Weekly Worksheet 8 • Page 31-32 • (LP)			
Week 9	Day 41	Read Page 61 • Saved from our enemies • (IFBS)			
	Day 42	Read Page 62-63 • Gideon becomes a warrior • (IFBS)			
	Day 43	Read Pages 64-65 • Strong enough to kill a lion / Samson falls in love • (IFBS)			
	Day 44	Read Page 66 • A caring daughter • (IFBS)			
	Day 45	Weekly Worksheet 9 • Pages 33-34 • (LP) Quiz 1 • Pages 113-114 • (LP)			
First Semester-Second Quarter					
Week 1	Day 46	Read Pages 67-68 • Hannah gives her baby to God / God calls Samuel • (IFBS)			
	Day 47	Read Page 69 • The ark seized in battle • (IFBS)			
	Day 48	Read Pages 70-71 • Kings of Israel • (IFBS)			
	Day 49	Read Pages 72-73 • We want a king! / Saul makes a mistake (IFBS)			
	Day 50	Weekly Worksheet 10 • Pages 35-38 • (LP)			
Week 2	Day 51	Read Pages 74-75 • A shepherd boy is chosen as king / David and Goliath • (IFBS)			
	Day 52	Read Pages 76-77 • Saul becomes jealous / A wife for David (IFBS)			
	Day 53	Read Pages 78-79 • Saul asks a witch to tell the future / David becomes king of Israel • (IFBS)			
	Day 54	Read Pages 80-81 • The ark comes to Jerusalem / Mephibosheth (IFBS)			
	Day 55	Weekly Worksheet 11 • Pages 39-42 • (LP)			
Week 3	Day 56	Read Page 82 • David takes another man's wife • (IFBS)			
	Day 57	Read Page 83 • Absalom dies in an oak tree • (IFBS)			
	Day 58	Read Pages 84-85 • Who will be the next king? / Clever King Solomon • (IFBS)			
	Day 59	Read Page 86 • Building the great temple • (IFBS)			
	Day 60	Weekly Worksheet 12 • Pages 43-46 • (LP)			

Date	Day	Assignment	Due Date	✓	Grade
Week 4	Day 61	Read Pages 87-88 • The Queen of Sheba / Solomon turns away from God • (IFBS)			
	Day 62	Read Pages 89-90 • A divided land / Elijah saves the widow and her son • (IFBS)			
	Day 63	Read Pages 91-92 • God's altar bursts into flames / Naboth's vineyard • (IFBS)			
	Day 64	Read Page 93 • Taken up to heaven • (IFBS)			
	Day 65	Weekly Worksheet 13 • Pages 47-48 • (LP)			
Week 5	Day 66	Read Pages 94-95 • Save my son! / Naaman is healed • (IFBS)			
	Day 67	Read Page 96 • Israel's final defeat • (IFBS)			
	Day 68	Read Page 97 • Judah's noble kings • (IFBS)			
	Day 69	Read Page 98 • David worships God • (IFBS)			
	Day 70	Weekly Worksheet 14 • Pages 49-50 • (LP)			
Week 6	Day 71	Read Pages 99-100 • Praises win the victory / The boy Joash is crowned king • (IFBS)			
	Day 72	Read Pages 101-102 • Raising the temple from its ruins / Jerusalem, a pile of rubble • (IFBS)			
	Day 73	Read Page 103 • The walls made strong again • (IFBS)			
	Day 74	Read Page 104 • God's people say sorry • (IFBS)			
	Day 75	Weekly Worksheet 15 • Pages 51-52 • (LP)			
Week 7	Day 76	Read Page 105 • Esther foils a plot • (IFBS)			
	Day 77	Read Page 106 • Job trusts his God• (IFBS)			
	Day 78	Read Pages 107-108 • The way of happiness / The Lord is my shepherd • (IFBS)			
	Day 79	Read Pages 109-110 • Where will I find help? / Everybody praise God • (IFBS)			
	Day 80	Weekly Worksheet 16 • Pages 53-54 • (LP)			
Week 8	Day 81	Read Pages 111-112 • Wise sayings / Life has a meaning? (IFBS)			
	Day 82	Read Page 113 • How beautiful you are! — Page 113 • (IFBS)			
	Day 83	Read Pages 114-115 • God calls Isaiah to be a prophet / Hezekiah cries for healing • (IFBS)			
	Day 84	Read Page 116 • God comforts His people • (IFBS)			
	Day 85	Weekly Worksheet 17 • Pages 55-58 • (LP)			
Week 9	Day 86	Read Pages 117-118 • The suffering servant / The potter shapes the clay • (IFBS)			
	Day 87	Read Page 119 • The good and bad figs • (IFBS)			
	Day 88	Read Page 120-121 • Jeremiah rewrites the scroll / Thrown into the well • (IFBS)			
	Day 89	Read Pages 122-123 • God's people in exile • (IFBS)			
	Day 90	Weekly Worksheet 18 • Pages 59-62 • (LP) Quiz 2 • Pages 115-116 • (LP)			
		Mid-Term Grade			

Second Semester Suggested Daily Schedule

Date	Day	Assignment	Due Date	✓	Grade
		Second Semester-Third Quarter			
Week 1	Day 91	Read Pages 124-125 • Ezekiel warns of God's anger / Dry bones come to life • (IFBS)			
	Day 92	Read Pages 126-127 • Trained for the king's service / Daniel explains the king's dream • (IFBS)			
	Day 93	Read Pages 128-129 • The fiery furnace / The writing on the wall • (IFBS)			
	Day 94	Read Pages 130-131 • Daniel in the lion's den • (IFBS)			
	Day 95	Weekly Worksheet 19 • Pages 63-66 • (LP)			
Week 2	Day 96	Read Pages 132-133 • God will pour out His Spirit / Be fair to my people • (IFBS)			
	Day 97	Read Pages 134-135 • A mighty fish swallows Jonah / God forgives Nineva • (IFBS)			
	Day 98	Read Pages 136-137 • Rebuild My temple / Walk in My ways (IFBS)			
	Day 99	Read Pages 138-139 • Why don't you honor Me / Returning to God • (IFBS)			
	Day 100	Weekly Worksheet 20 • Pages 67-68 • (LP)			
Week 3	Day 101	Read Pages 140-143 • Introduction - New Testament • (IFBS)			
	Day 102	Read Page 144 • Zechariah is promised a son • (IFBS)			
	Day 103	Read Page 145 • An angel brings news for Mary • (IFBS)			
	Day 104	Read Page 146 • God reassures Joseph • (IFBS)			
	Day 105	Weekly Worksheet 21 • Pages 69-70 • (LP)			
Week 4	Day 106	Read Pages 147-148 • Born in a stable / The shepherds and the wise men • (IFBS)			
	Day 107	Read Pages 149-150 • Great rejoicing! / Escape from Herod (IFBS)			
	Day 108	Read Page 151 • In My Father's house • (IFBS)			
	Day 109	Read Pages 152-153 • John baptizes Jesus / The devil tempts Jesus • (IFBS)			
	Day 110	Weekly Worksheet 22 • Pages 71-72 • (LP)			
Week 5	Day 111	Read Pages 154-155 • The ministry of Jesus • (IFBS)			
	Day 112	Read Page 156 • The Spirit of God is on Me • (IFBS)			
	Day 113	Read Page 157 • Follow Me • (IFBS)			
	Day 114	Read Page 158 • Water becomes wine • (IFBS)			
	Day 115	Weekly Worksheet 23 • Pages 73-74 • (LP)			
Week 6	Day 116	Read Pages 159-160 • Jesus heals the lepers / The centurion's servant • (IFBS)			
	Day 117	Read Page 161 • Jesus forgives sins • (IFBS)			
	Day 118	Read Pages 162-163 • Lord of the Sabbath / The water of eternal life • (IFBS)			
	Day 119	Read Pages 164-165 • The Sermon on the Mount • (IFBS)			
	Day 120	Weekly Worksheet 24 • Pages 75-76 • (LP)			

Date	Day	Assignment	Due Date	✓	Grade
Week 7	Day 121	Read Pages 166-167 • Building on the rock / Jesus calms the storm • (IFBS)			
	Day 122	Read Pages 168-169 • Raising the dead / Anger in the temple (IFBS)			
	Day 123	Read Page 170 • You must be born again • (IFBS)			
	Day 124	Read Page 171 • Jesus sends out His Disciples • (IFBS)			
	Day 125	Weekly Worksheet 25 • Pages 77-78 • (LP)			
Week 8	Day 126	Read Pages 172-173 • The sower and the soils / Jesus teaches us to pray • (IFBS)			
	Day 127	Read Pages 174-175 • Give me his head! • (IFBS)			
	Day 128	Read Page 176 • Jesus feeds the hungry crowd • (IFBS)			
	Day 129	Read Pages 177-178 • Come to Me, Peter / A woman's faith (IFBS)			
	Day 130	Weekly Worksheet 26 • Pages 79-80 • (LP)			
Week 9	Day 131	Read Page 179 • Jesus is glorified • (IFBS)			
	Day 132	Read Pages 180-181 • The good Samaritan / The great wedding feast • (IFBS)			
	Day 133	Read Pages 182-183 • Looking for the lost / Welcome home (IFBS)			
	Day 134	Read Page 184 • The good shepherd • (IFBS)			
	Day 135	Weekly Worksheet 27 • Pages 81-82 • (LP) Quiz 3 • Pages 117-118 • (LP)			
		Second Semester-Fourth Quarter			
Week 1	Day 136	Read Page 185 • Coming to Jesus • (IFBS)			
	Day 137	Read Pages 186-187 • Lazarus brought back to life / Who deserves forgiveness? • (IFBS)			
	Day 138	Read Pages 188-189 • Come down, Zacchaeus / All treated the same • (IFBS)			
	Day 139	Read Page 190 • She gave all she had • (IFBS)			
	Day 140	Weekly Worksheet 28 • Pages 83-86 • (LP)			
Week 2	Day 141	Read Page 191 • The wise and foolish girls • (IFBS)			
	Day 142	Read Pages 192-193 • The talents / The sheep and the goats (IFBS)			
	Day 143	Read Pages 194-195 • Jesus arrives in Jerusalem / The sign of Christ's return • (IFBS)			
	Day 144	Read Pages 196-197 • The last supper • (IFBS)			
	Day 145	Weekly Worksheet 29 • Pages 87-90 • (LP)			
Week 3	Day 146	Read Pages 198-199 • Do not be afraid / Arrested in the garden • (IFBS)			
	Day 147	Read Pages 200-201 • The priests accuse Jesus / Peter disowns Jesus • (IFBS)			
	Day 148	Read Page 202 • Pilate judges Jesus • (IFBS)			
	Day 149	Read Page 203 • Nailed to a Cross • (IFBS)			
	Day 150	Weekly Worksheet 30 • Pages 91-92 • (LP)			

Date	Day	Assignment	Due Date	✓	Grade
Week 4	Day 151	Read Page 204 • Jesus is alive! • (IFBS)			
	Day 152	Read Page 205 • Jesus appears to the Disciples • (IFBS)			
	Day 153	Read Pages 206-207 • Thomas is not sure / Breakfast with Jesus • (IFBS)			
	Day 154	Read Pages 208-209 • Jesus enters heaven / The Holy Spirit comes • (IFBS)			
	Day 155	Weekly Worksheet 31 • Pages 93-94 • (LP)			
Week 5	Day 156	Read Pages 210-211 • The first Christians • (IFBS)			
	Day 157	Read Pages 212-213 • The first Christian believers / Peter heals the beggar • (IFBS)			
	Day 158	Read Pages 214-215 • Ananias and Sapphira tell lies / Philip and the Ethiopian • (IFBS)			
	Day 159	Read Pages 216-217 • Jesus challenges Saul • (IFBS)			
	Day 160	Weekly Worksheet 32 • Pages 95-96 • (LP)			
Week 6	Day 161	Read Pages 218-219 • God's love is for everyone / An Angel frees Peter • (IFBS)			
	Day 162	Read Pages 220-221 • Sharing the good news with others / An earthquake shakes the prison • (IFBS)			
	Day 163	Read Pages 222-223 • Arguing with his enemies / Shipwrecked on the way to Rome • (IFBS)			
	Day 164	Read Pages 224-225 • In a right relationship / God's armor protects us • (IFBS)			
	Day 165	Weekly Worksheet 33 • Pages 97-100 • (LP)			
Week 7	Day 166	Read Pages 226-227 • Using our spiritual gifts / We will live again • (IFBS)			
	Day 167	Read Pages 228-229 • The Second Coming / Letters to church leaders • (IFBS)			
	Day 168	Read Pages 230-231 • The importance of faith / Living for God • (IFBS)			
	Day 169	Read Pages 232-233 • John's vision of heaven / A new heaven and earth • (IFBS)			
	Day 170	Weekly Worksheet 34 • Pages 101-104 • (LP) Quiz 4 • Pages 119-120 • (LP)			
Week 8	Day 171	Read Pages 234-237 • Daily Life in OT times • (IFBS)			
	Day 172	Read Pages 238-239 • Daily Life in NT times • IFBS			
	Day 173	Read Pages 240-241 • Plants and animals in the Bible • (IFBS)			
	Day 174	Read Pages 242-243 • The Holy Land • (IFBS)			
	Day 175	Weekly Worksheet 35 • Pages 105-108 • (LP)			
Week 9	Day 176	Read Pages 244-245 • Other Bible lands • (IFBS)			
	Day 177	Read Pages 246-247 • Who's who in the Bible • (IFBS)			
	Day 178	Weekly Worksheet 36 • Pages 109-110 • (LP)			
	Day 179	Test your knowledge 1 • Pages 123-124 • (LP)			
	Day 180	Test your knowledge 2 • Pages 125-126 • (LP)			
		Final Grade			

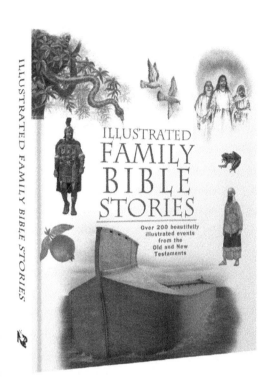

Elementary Bible and Grammar Worksheets

for Use with

Illustrated Family Bible Stories

I. VERSE OF THE WEEK

"In the beginning was the Word, and the Word was with God, and the Word was God" (John 1:1).

II. VOCABULARY WORDS

Write a definition for each of the following words. You may use a dictionary.

Pentateuch

descendant

integrity

genre

testament

III. GENRE

The Bible is a collection of 66 separate books. These are in two main sections, the Old Testament and the New Testament, which are further divided into genres of literature.

1. The genres of the Old Testament are:
a. _the Law_, b. _history_, c. _poetry_, d. _prophecy_.

2. The genres of the New Testament are:
a. _history_, b. _Letters_, c. _prophecy_.

IV. COMPREHENSION AND MEMORIZATION

1. Write a short description of each of the genres used in the Old Testament.

a. The Law:_____.

b. History:_____.

c. Poetry:_____.

d. Prophecy:_____.

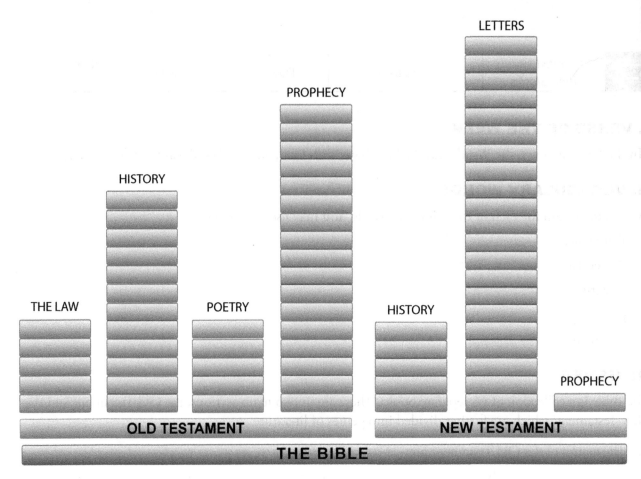

4. Fill in the blanks with the following words:

1 Chronicles	2 Thessalonians	Galatians	Jude	Philippians
1 Corinthians	2 Timothy	Genesis	Judges	Proverbs
1 John	3 John	Habakkuk	Lamentations	Psalms
1 Kings	Acts	Haggai	Leviticus	Revelation
1 Peter	Amos	Hebrews	Luke	Romans
1 Samuel	Colossians	Hosea	Malachi	Ruth
1 Thessalonians	Daniel	Isaiah	Mark	Song of Songs
1 Timothy	Deuteronomy	James	Matthew	Titus
2 Chronicles	Ecclesiastes	Jeremiah	Micah	Zechariah
2 Corinthians	Ephesians	Job	Nahum	Zephaniah
2 John	Esther	Joel	Nehemiah	
2 Kings	Exodus	John	Numbers	
2 Peter	Ezekiel	Jonah	Obadiah	
2 Samuel	Ezra	Joshua	Philemon	

V. ACTIVITY

Choose one of the genres from question 3 above and write a short paper about your family that matches the genre. For instance, if you choose the Law, you could write about your family origin and culture.

VI. BIBLE SCHOLARS

Memorize what God did on each day of creation. Give an oral report to your family, describing each day of creation. You may also want to draw a picture of each day to display as you describe it to your family.

I. VERSE OF THE WEEK

Then God said, "Let us make mankind in our image, in our likeness, so that they may rule over the fish in the sea and the birds in the sky, over the livestock and all the wild animals, and over all the creatures that move along the ground" (Genesis 1:26).

II. VOCABULARY WORDS

Write a definition for each of the following words. You may use a dictionary.

biblia

prophetic vision

salvation

paradise

cunning

III. GRAMMAR REVIEW: NOUNS

A noun is one of the eight common parts of speech in the English language. All words are classified into one of these parts of speech based upon their meaning and/or use in a sentence.

A common noun names any person, place, or thing. Examples: fruit, animal, stars

A proper noun is the name of a specific person, place, or thing. Examples: God, Old Testament, Eden

1. Underline the common nouns and circle the proper nouns in the following sentences:

   a. The Bible is a collection of many books of different kinds of writing.

   b. The Bible has one central message: God's salvation of His people.

   c. God made a beautiful garden called Eden, a paradise full of animals and fruit trees.

2. Think of a proper noun that goes with each of the common nouns listed below. Write it in the space provided:

   a. god   _____

   b. garden   _____

   c. woman   _____

   d. prophet   _____

   e. book   _____

   f. country   _____

   g. day   _____

IV. COMPREHENSION AND MEMORIZATION

3. Read all the way through the story on page 16 of your book. Who were the main characters in this story? What did they do? Where? When? Why? On a separate piece of paper, retell the story in your own words, answering the above questions. Underline the common nouns and circle the proper nouns in your story.

4. Can you relate to the story of Adam and Eve? Does it remind you of a time or event in your own life? Read 1 John 1:9, Isaiah 43:25, and Psalm 103:10–12, and then write a prayer or a poem expressing your feelings about God's forgiving nature.

V. ACTIVITY

Walk around your house and yard, and see if you can find items that begin with each letter of the alphabet. Be sure to write them down in alphabetical order. How many common nouns did you find? How many proper nouns?

VI. GRAMMAR SCHOLARS

Using the nouns you gathered around your house and yard, write a paragraph or two describing your house and yard using the nouns you found. Remember to capitalize the proper nouns.

I. VERSE OF THE WEEK

Abraham will surely become a great and powerful nation, and all nations on earth will be blessed through him" (Genesis 18:18).

II. VOCABULARY WORDS

Write a definition for each of the following words. You may use a dictionary.

nomad

adze

chisel

gangway

sophisticated

III. GRAMMAR REVIEW: MAIN VERBS

A verb is a word that shows action or a state of being. Every sentence in the English language contains at least one verb. In this lesson we are going to focus on main verbs or "action" verbs.

Main verbs describe what someone or something is doing or feeling.

Examples of main verbs:

Water poured down from the sky.	"poured" is a main verb because it describes what the water is doing.
Noah obeyed God.	"obeyed" is a main verb because it describes what Noah was doing.
Abraham believed in God.	"believed" is a main verb because it describes how Abraham was feeling.

1. Underline the main verbs in the following sentences:
   a. God appeared to Abraham in a vision.
   b. Abraham trembled before God.
   c. Sarah treated Hagar unkindly.
   d. God sent angels to destroy the city.

2. Use the main verbs in the table to complete the following sentences:

| located | pulled | transformed |
| believed | gathered | run |

   a. Sodom and Gomorrah were once _____ near the Dead Sea.
   b. _____ into the hills!
   c. The angels _____ Lot into the house.

d. A large crowd of men _____ outside Lot's house.

e. Abraham _____ what God told him.

f. Lot's wife was _____ into a pillar of salt.

IV. COMPREHENSION AND MEMORIZATION

3. Read all the way through the story on page 25 of your book. Who were the main characters in this story? What did they do? Where? When? Why? On a separate piece of paper, retell the story in your own words, answering the above questions. Underline the main verbs in your story.

4. What lessons can you learn from the characters in this story? Try to write down at least three lessons that you can share with your family.

V. ACTIVITY

5. Remember, a main verb is a word that shows action or a feeling. For the next few minutes, observe a person or a pet in your vicinity and list everything you observe them doing or feeling. How many main verbs did you write down?

VI. GRAMMAR SCHOLARS

Write a story about the person or pet you observed in your activity. Remember to use the main verbs you wrote down.

. VERSE OF THE WEEK

Stay in this land for a while, and I will be with you and will bless you. For to you and your descendants I will give all these lands and will confirm the oath I swore to your father Abraham" (Genesis 26:3).

I. VOCABULARY WORDS

Write a definition for each of the following words. You may use a dictionary.

sacrifice

inheritance

cunning

lentil

agreement

II. GRAMMAR REVIEW: HELPING VERBS

Helping verbs come before the main verb in a sentence. They "help" us understand the main verb in the sentence by showing time and meaning, but they do not have meaning on their own. If your friend called you on the phone and said, "I was," you probably wouldn't understand what he was trying to communicate. While "was" is a verb, it is not a verb that stands alone. "I was petting the cat" or "I was watching a movie" are examples of statements that make more sense. Petting and watching are the main action and "was" helps us understand the action.

Other examples of **helping verbs** in a sentence:

| Your family must leave Haran. | "must" is a helping verb because it is not something that can be done on its own — but it helps us understand the main verb "leave" |
| Ruins were found all over Mesopotamia. | "were" is a helping verb because it is not something that can be done on its own — but it helps us understand the main verb "found" |

1. Circle the **helping verbs** in the following sentences:

    a. I will give this land to you and your many descendants.

    b. Jacob was amazed that God had spoken to him.

    c. I have seen God face to face and am still alive!

    d. I am trusting that God will provide a sacrifice.

    e. Sarah had been listening to their conversation.

List of helping verbs:

am, are, is, was, were, be, being, been

have, has, had

shall, will

do, does, did

may, must, might

can, could, would, should

2. Choose a helping verb from the above list to complete the following sentences:

a. Why did Jacob run away after he stole Esau's blessing?

Because he _____ afraid.

b. What did Abraham tell his servant when he sent him to find a wife for Isaac?

God _____ help him find the right woman.

c. Why did Abraham send his servant to Mesopotamia to find a wife for Isaac?

He _____ not want him to marry a woman from Canaan.

IV. COMPREHENSION AND MEMORIZATION

3. Memorize the **helping verbs**. To make it more fun you can sing them to the tune of "Jingle Bells"!

Helping verbs,

Helping verbs,

There are 23,

Am is are was and were

Being been and be

Have has had,

Do does did

Shall will should and would

There are five more helping verbs

May might must can could

4. Esau was very angry with Jacob for stealing his blessing. Put yourself in Esau's shoes. How would you have reacted? In the end, Esau forgave his brother. Can you think of a time when you were angry with someone for what they said or did? Have you forgiven them? Read Colossians 3:13 and Ephesians 4:31–32. If necessary, ask God to help you forgive them. There are also times when we need to ask someone to forgive us for something we have done or said. Read Matthew 5:23–24 and Matthew 5:9. Asking for forgiveness can be hard to do, but God will give you the strength (Ephesians 3:16)!

V. ACTIVITY

Make a poster listing all of the **helping verbs**. Hang it in your room to help you remember them.

VI. GRAMMAR SCHOLARS

It is important to know which **helping verb** to use in a sentence.
Use the verb **"is"** when referring to one person or thing.
Use the verb **"are"** when referring to more than one person or thing.

Examples:
Daniel **is** thrown into the lion's den.
The lions **are** kept from harming Daniel.

Use the verb **"was"** when referring to one.
Use the verb **"were"** when referring to more than one.

Examples:
King Darius **was** anxious all night.
The wicked officials **were** thrown to the lions.

Use the verb **"has"** when referring to one.
Use the verb **"have"** when referring to more than one.

Examples:
Daniel **has** courage.
The angels **have** shut the lion's mouths.

Write a sentence for each verb tense.

a. is:

b. are:

c. was:

d. were:

e. has:

f. have:

. VERSE OF THE WEEK

You intended to harm me, but God intended it for good to accomplish what is now being done, the saving
f many lives" (Genesis 50:20).

I. VOCABULARY WORDS

flocks

calamity

signet

famine

sieve

II. GRAMMAR REVIEW: SENTENCE STRUCTURE — SUBJECT AND PREDICATE

entences can have many parts, but even the most simple sentence will contain a subject and a predicate.
he subject tells who or what the sentence is about. The predicate is what is being said about the subject.
he word *predicate* means "to declare." A predicate will always contain a verb. You need both a subject and a
predicate in a sentence in order to express a complete thought. Example:

Jacob had twelve sons.

Jacob is who the sentence is about — so Jacob is the subject.

What is being said or declared about Jacob? He had twelve sons — so had twelve sons is the predicate.

. Underline the subject and circle the predicate in the following sentences:

a. Joseph had an unusual dream.

b. Joseph's brothers were jealous of him.

c. The Ishmaelite traders sold Joseph as a slave.

d. Our father has already lost Joseph.

e. The Egyptian people were in danger of starving.

. Write five simple sentences of your own. Underline the subject and circle the predicate.

a.

b.

c.

d.

e.

IV. COMPREHENSION AND MEMORIZATION

3. Read the story on page 37 of your book. Fill in the blanks in the following sentences with an appropriate subject or predicate based on this story. Your answers do not need to match the book word for word; just write a subject or predicate that tells the same story.

   a. _____ was sent to the fields to check on his brothers.

   b. Joseph's brothers _____.

   c. _____ did not want to kill Joseph.

   d. Joseph's coat _____.

   e. Jacob _____.

4. Joseph's story seemed sad at first, but in time it was apparent that God caused good to come out of his misfortune. Can you think of a time when God brought good out of a difficult situation in your life? Read Romans 8:28 and then write a poem or a prayer expressing your feelings about God's goodness.

V. ACTIVITY

Create a fun card game to play with your friends and family! Take a package of index cards and on half of them write a simple subject such as "David" or "the dog," and on the other half write some simple predicates such as "loves to eat ice cream" or "barked all night long." Mark the back of the index card with either an "S" for subject or a "P" for predicate. Place the stacks of "S" and "P" cards face down on the table. Take turns drawing one from each stack and read your sentence out loud. Shuffle and repeat. Have fun!

VI. GRAMMAR SCHOLARS

A compound predicate tells us two or more things about the same subject. There is only one subject in a compound predicate.

Example:

Joseph ate supper and left for the fields.

Joseph is the subject. The sentence tells us two things about Joseph — he ate supper and he left for the fields.

Fill in the blanks in the following sentences with a compound predicate.

   a. Joseph _____.

   b. Joseph's brothers _____.

   c. Joseph's coat _____.

   d. Jacob _____.

   e. Pharaoh _____.

. VERSE OF THE WEEK

The LORD said, 'I have indeed seen the misery of my people in Egypt. I have heard them crying out because of their slave drivers, and I am concerned about their suffering'" (Exodus 3:7).

I. VOCABULARY WORDS

overrule

headdress

pharaoh

exodus

plague

II. GRAMMAR REVIEW: PRONOUNS

A **pronoun** takes the place of a noun. Pronouns can take the place of people or things.

Look at the difference between the same sentence written with and without a pronoun.

"The king of Egypt was frightened by the many Israelites living in his country."

"The king of Egypt was frightened by the many Israelites living in the king's country."

"When Moses grew up, he left Egypt and became a shepherd."

"When Moses grew up, Moses left Egypt and became a shepherd."

1. Write in the correct pronouns.

a. During each plague the king said that the people could leave, but when Moses stopped it, _____ changed his mind.

b. Early next morning the king sent messengers to Moses, pleading with _____ to leave.

c. The descendants of Jacob — the twelve tribes of Israel — increased in number when _____ settled in Egypt.

d. Everything had to be portable, so that _____ could be easily transported.

e. After forty years in the Sinai desert the Israelites probably went south, but _____ do not know _____ exact route.

IV. COMPREHENSION AND MEMORIZATION

2. Write five sentences using pronouns for each word given.

a. Miriam:

b. bush:

c. Moses and Aaron:

d. Israelites:

e. Jacob:

3. List the ten plagues God sent upon Egypt.

   a.   f.

   b.   g.

   c.   h.

   d.   i.

   e.   j.

4. What did each of these plagues demonstrate God is supreme over? (Hint: page 44 in your book.)

5. Think about the last plague. If you do not remember the details, re-read page 43 in your book.

   Read Luke 22:7–20. In this passage, Jesus celebrates Passover with His disciples.

   Read Luke 23:33–49. In this passage, Jesus became the Passover Lamb by sacrificing His own life for us.

   Read Luke 24:33–43. Jesus conquers death and is raised from the dead.

   The Jewish people celebrated Passover, remembering how God delivered them from the last plague in Egypt. Jesus celebrated Passover before He died and was raised to life. Jesus gave us instructions about celebrating Passover in Luke 22:7–20. What do we call the Passover feast we celebrate today?

6. God directed the Israelites through the desert. He provided for the Israelites when they came to the Red Sea, and also when they were hungry and thirsty. Write a list of all of the ways God provides for you. Remember to thank Him.

V. ACTIVITY

Draw the map on page 45 of your book. Label the countries, cities, etc. Draw the route you think the Israelites took.

VI. BIBLE SCHOLARS

Celebrate Passover with your family in a similar way the Bible describes in Exodus 12:1–28. Discuss your plans with a parent. Decide how detailed you want to be with your celebration. Do you want to go without eating anything made with yeast for seven days? Do you want to cook real lamb over a fire? No matter how simple or elaborate your family celebrates the Passover, think about how the Israelites may have felt as they followed the Lord's directions. Write a paragraph or two about your celebration.

I. VERSE OF THE WEEK

"I am the LORD your God, who brought you out of Egypt, out of the land of slavery" (Exodus 20:2).

II. VOCABULARY WORDS

ordination

scrolls

festival

rebel

III. GRAMMAR REVIEW: ADJECTIVES

An **adjective** is a word that describes a noun. Adjectives may clarify which one, how many, what color, size, shape, taste, look, feel, sound, mood, age, time, and quality. An adjective is usually located before the noun it describes.

Example:

Aaron collected *beautiful* jewelry from the Israelites to make a *golden* calf.

The word *beautiful* describes the jewelry. The word *golden* describes the calf.

Without adjectives, the sentence would be less interesting and specific.

Aaron collected jewelry from the Israelites to make a calf.

1. Give an **adjective** to describe each noun:

a. Moses:

b. manna:

c. Israelites:

d. snake:

e. donkey:

2. Write two sentences of your own using at least four **adjectives** to describe the land of Canaan. Circle the **adjectives** you used.

a.

b.

IV. COMPREHENSION AND MEMORIZATION

3. Write out the Ten Commandments.

a.   f.

b.   g.

c.   h.

d.   i.

e.   j.

4. Read Matthew 22:36–40. Write out the two commandments Jesus says all of the laws are based on.

   a.

   b.

5. Can you imagine having a donkey talk to you? In this account, words are very important. Balak wanted Balaam to curse (say evil things against) the Israelites. A donkey and an angel warn Balaam. Rather than cursing the Israelites, Balaam uses his words to bless them. Can you think of a time you wanted to say bad things about someone? Sometimes it is hard to say good things about a person we are angry with. What good things can you think of to say about that person? Ask God to help you. Write out the good things you think of and ask God to bless them.

V. ACTIVITY

Play a fun game of "I Spy!" with a family member. Pick an object in the room and say, "I spy with my little eyes. . . ." Go on to describe the object using only adjectives. See how long it takes the person to guess what object you are describing.

VI. GRAMMAR SCHOLARS

Adjectives make writing interesting.

   a. Pick a topic and write a paragraph. You may want to describe a family member, a pet, or a place you like to visit.

   b. Write your paragraph again, adding adjective that describe feelings, personality, or appearance.

   c. How did your paragraph change? Which paragraph was more interesting?

I. VERSE OF THE WEEK

Be strong and courageous. Do not be afraid or terrified because of them, for the LORD your God goes with you; he will never leave you nor forsake you" (Deuteronomy 31:6).

II. VOCABULARY WORDS

commission

prophet

scarlet

inhabitants

allocated

judgment

III. GRAMMAR REVIEW: ADVERBS

An **adverb** is a word that describes a verb, an adjective, or another adverb. Adverbs tell how, when, where, why, how often, and how much. They also tell how much or how little, when, where, why, how long, and how often. Many adverbs end with -ly.

Example:

Joshua *secretly* called two men and told them to go and spy out the land.

The word *"secretly"* describes the verb *"called."*

Without the adverb, the sentence is missing important information.

Joshua called two men and told them to go and spy out the land.

1. Underline the **adverb** in each sentence.

   a. Moses, you will soon die.

   b. Slowly he climbed Mount Nebo.

   c. God will certainly give us the land.

   d. They marched silently around the walls of the city.

   e. They were easily defeated by the inhabitants.

2. Retell the story of Rahab on page 56. Use at least four **adverbs** in your description. Circle the **adverbs** you used.

IV. COMPREHENSION AND MEMORIZATION

3. Make a list of the 12 tribes of Israel.

a.   g.

b.   h.

c.   i.

d.   j.

e.   k.

f.   l.

4. Who were the 12 tribes named after?

5. Marching around a city is a strange way to capture it. How do you think Joshua felt about telling the Israelite's God's plan to destroy Jericho? Do you think he was nervous? Do you think he wondered if the people would listen and obey? Do you think he might have been scared they would think he was crazy? Ask one of your parents or family members to tell you about a time God asked them to do something others might not understand. How did they feel about it? Did they obey? What happened? How do you think you would have felt in the same situation? Use these questions to help describe the experience.

V. ACTIVITY

Play a fun game of "Charades" with family members. On note cards, write at least a dozen verbs, one verb per card. Write an equal number of adverbs on note cards. Label the back sides of your cards so they do not get mixed up. Shuffle your two decks of cards and place them in two upside-down piles. Pick one verb and one adverb. Act out your selection and see who can guess the verb/adverb combination you are acting out.

VI. GRAMMAR SCHOLARS

Remember, an **adverb** is a word that describes a verb, an adjective, or another adverb. Adverbs tell how, when, where, why, how often, and how much. They also tell how much or how little, when, where, why, how long, and how often. Many, but not all, adverbs end with -*ly*. Examples include fast, never, and very.

Make a list of at least ten adverbs that do not end in –ly. (Hint: You may need a dictionary or to ask a parent to look online.)

a.   f.

b.   g.

c.   h.

d.   i.

e.   j.

I. VERSE OF THE WEEK

May the LORD repay you for what you have done. May you be richly rewarded by the LORD, the God of Israel, under whose wings you have come to take refuge" (Ruth 2:12).

II. VOCABULARY WORDS

oppression

insignificant

summoned

lair

gleaning

III. GRAMMAR REVIEW: PREPOSITIONS

Prepositions show a relationship between nouns, pronouns, and other words in a sentence. They are usually found before a noun and are part of a phrase.

Example: **He presented a gift <u>to</u> the king.**

The word *"to"* is the preposition. It shows the relationship of the king to the gift.

"King" is the object of the preposition. *"To the king"* is called a prepositional phrase.

Common **prepositions** include:

about	before	for	off	through
above	behind	from	on	to
after	between	in	out	under
around	by	like	over	until
as	down	near	since	upon
at	during	of	than	with

1. Create five **prepositional phrases**, starting with words from the list of common **prepositions**.

   a.

   b.

   c.

   d.

   e.

2. Use the prepositional phrases you wrote to write five complete sentences. Underline the propositional phrase and circle the object of the preposition

   a.

   b.

   c.

   d.

   e.

IV. COMPREHENSION AND MEMORIZATION

3. Identify the correct person for each description.

    a. A Nazirite _____

    b. A left-handed man _____

    c. Her sons died _____

    d. Pulled down the altar to Baal _____

    e. The woman Samson revealed his secret to _____

    f. The man who married Ruth _____

    g. Gave God's instructions to Barak about attacking Sisera _____

    h. With a handful of men, defeated the Midianites _____

4. An angel appeared to Gideon and announced that the Lord was with him and then called him a mighty warrior. Think about how you would feel if you were taking out the garbage for your parents and an angel met you at the end of the driveway and called you a mighty warrior! Even though Gideon was the youngest member of his family and his family was the smallest tribe in the whole nation, God told Gideon He would use him to defeat the enemy army. Then, before the battle could begin, God shrank the number of people fighting for the Israelites. Why do you suppose God did this? (Hint: Read the section "Winning against the odds" on page 62.) Gideon felt insignificant and his army was small in comparison to the enemy. On top of that, they went into battle with trumpets, jars, and torches. Do you sometimes feel like you are too young or insignificant to do something for God? Draw a picture of Gideon's army going into battle with their unique fighting strategy. While you are drawing your picture, think about God's power. Think about how He will use you to accomplish His battles and give you great victories if you trust and obey Him. Pray and ask God to help you accomplish His will. Show your drawing to your parents and explain to them what you have learned from the life of Gideon.

V. ACTIVITY

Gather your family and play a game of Simon Says using prepositional phrases.

    Examples:

    Simon says put your hands *on your head.*

    Simon says put your hands *under your knees.*

When someone is caught doing something Simon didn't say, you can give them another chance if they can identify the prepositional phrase. Have fun!

VI. GRAMMAR SCHOLARS

Prepositions are always found in a phrase. A prepositional phrase contains the preposition and the noun it refers to.

For each sentence underline the prepositional phrase if it has one.

a. Ruth stayed by Naomi's side.

b. Ruth set the grain down.

c. Ruth slept near Boaz's feet.

d. Boaz held up his shoe.

e. Boaz took off his shoe.

I. VERSE OF THE WEEK

The LORD was with Samuel as he grew up, and he let none of Samuel's words fall to the ground" 1 Samuel 3:19).

II. VOCABULARY WORDS

synagogue

rabbi

Bar Mitzvah

anoint

covenant

III. GRAMMAR REVIEW: POSSESSION

Possession shows ownership.

For most **singular** and **plural** nouns add 's.

Example:

Gideon's trumpet was loud.

There is only one Gideon so that means Gideon is a singular noun.

The 's shows that the trumpet belongs to Gideon.

The men's trumpet was loud.

The word *men* means there are many men so it is a plural noun.

The 's shows that the trumpet belongs to the men.

For **singular** and **plural** nouns that end in s only add the apostrophe.

Example:

James' trumpet was loud.

James is a singular noun that ends in **s**. We add only the apostrophe after the **s**.

The boys' trumpet was loud.

Boys are a plural noun because there is more than one boy. Since it ends in s, we add only the apostrophe to the plural noun.

You should add 's to **indefinite pronouns**. Indefinite pronouns end in **body** or **one**.

Example:

Someone's trumpet was loud.

Someone is an indefinite pronoun. We add 's to the indefinite pronoun.

1. Write three sentences using regular possessive nouns.

    a.

    b.

    c.

2. Write three sentences using plural possessive nouns.

    a.

    b.

    c.

IV. COMPREHENSION AND MEMORIZATION

3. Answer the questions.

    a. Who did Eli, the priest, think was drunk? _____

    b. What name did Hannah give to the baby that she promised to consecrate to the Lord, and what doe
        that name mean? _____ _____

    c. Describe the menorah and tell what it symbolized.

    d. Why did God judge the family of Eli?

    e. In the Old Testament, the ark of the covenant held the presence of the Lord. What happened when
        the ark of the covenant was captured and put into the temple of the Philistines' god statue?

    f. Who were the first three kings of Israel? _____, _____,
        _____

    g. Why did God take the kingdom away from Saul and his children?

4. How did the people reject God when Samuel set his sons up as judges?

. Study the list of *Kings and Queens of Israel* from page 71. How many kings in all are listed?

. Can you guess how many of the kings, other than the first three (Saul, David, and Solomon), were good kings and obeyed the Lord?

. Was having a king a good thing for Israel? Did having a king help the people serve God better?

. Look up Isaiah 55:8–9 and write the verses here:

. How do you think the Israelites would have been better off if they had done things God's way?

10. Can you think of a time you were disobedient and things didn't work out so well? How would it have been different if you had obeyed? Can you think about a time when you did obey? Was it hard to obey? What good things happened that you may not have expected because you did obey? Write about both of your experiences. Tell which way worked out the best.

V. ACTIVITY

Play a game of Noun Slap with one or more members of your family. The rules are the same as Slap Jack with some special differences.

On a stack of at least 40 note cards, write a regular noun on each card.

On three more cards, write plural nouns that end in **s**.

On three more cards, write singular nouns that end in **s**.

On two more cards write a word that ends with **body** and **one**.

On seven more cards write the words: his, hers, its, ours, yours, theirs, whose

Mix the cards all up. Deal the cards face down between all of the players.

The person to the left of the dealer goes first. That person picks up the deck in front of them and quickly places the cards, one at a time, face up on the center of the table.

The players should keep watch for cards that do not require 's or only require an apostrophe. When the players see such a word, they slap the card as quickly as they can to beat their opponents. Rather than yell "Slap Jack!" they will yell either "NO Apostrophe S" or "Apostrophe Only!" If the player is correct, they keep the whole pile of cards, making sure they mix them up well with the card they already have. If they are wrong, they give up one of their cards to the player dealing the cards.

The player to win all of the cards wins. Have fun!

VI. GRAMMAR SCHOLARS

Do NOT add 's to **possessive pronouns** or **regular plural forms** of nouns.

Do not add 's to: his, hers, its, ours, yours, theirs, whose

Example:

His trumpet was loud.

His is a pronoun. We do not add 's to the pronoun.

Write three sentences using possessive pronouns.

a.

b.

c.

I. VERSE OF THE WEEK

"But the LORD said to Samuel, 'Do not consider his appearance or his height, for I have rejected him. The LORD does not look at the things people look at. People look at the outward appearance, but the LORD looks at the heart' " (1 Samuel 16:7).

II. VOCABULARY WORDS

regretted

jealous

treacherously

obscurity

gratitude

III. GRAMMAR REVIEW: CONTRACTIONS

Contractions are two words shortened into one. Where letters are left out, an apostrophe is used. Contractions are used in informal writing, such as writing a letter to a friend.

Example:

We'll is a contraction of we will. There is an apostrophe where letters are missing.

Can't is a contraction of can not. There is an apostrophe where letters are missing.

1. Combine the two words to create a contraction. Remember to us an apostrophe where letters are missing.

   a. That is

   b. We are

   c. Should not

   d. We would

   e. They have

2. Write three sentences using contractions.

   a.

   b.

   c.

IV. COMPREHENSION AND MEMORIZATION

3. Answer the questions.

a. How many sons did Jesse have?

b. Which son did God choose for Samuel to anoint as the new king of Israel?

c. How tall was Goliath?

d. About how tall do you think David was when he faced Goliath? (Hint: Ask your parents about how tall an average teenager is.)

e. What did Goliath rely on in the battle?

f. What did David rely on in the battle?

g. How did Saul feel about David becoming a national hero?

h. Who insulted David after David and his men had been kind to his servants? What happened to him?

i. Who then became David's wife?

j. What city did David make the capital of Israel?

k. Who did David make the leader of the army?

l. Who wanted to build the temple? Who did God say would build the temple?

m. Name the lame son of Jonathan that David showed kindness to.

. Read the section on page 76 about jealousy. Have you ever been jealous? Can you think of some things that can help you avoid being jealous? Write a letter to Saul, giving him your advice on how to stop being jealous of David.

V. ACTIVITY

Improve your memory while practicing contractions. You may play this game alone or with a family member.

Divide a stack of 20 note cards into two piles.

Take a card from one pile and write a contraction on it.

Take a card from the other pile and write out the two full words the contraction represents.

Continue this until all of the cards are written on.

Shuffle all of the cards into one pile.

Spread the cards upside down into rows of five.

Flip one card over.

Find another card to flip over.

See if the cards match the contraction with the two words it represents.

If it does, you keep the two cards and try again.

If it doesn't, turn the cards upside down again. Your turn is over and the next person gets a chance.

Keep playing until all of the contraction matches have been found.

The player who has the most cards in the end wins. If you are playing by yourself, set a timer and see if you can improve the amount of time it takes to find all of the matches. Have fun!

VI. GRAMMAR SCHOLARS

Write a list of 20 common contractions.

1.

2.

3.

4.

5.

6.

7.

8.

9.

10.

11.

12.

13.

14.

15.

16.

17.

18.

19.

20.

I. VERSE OF THE WEEK

And if you walk in obedience to me and keep my decrees and commands as David your father did, I will give you a long life" (1 Kings 3:14).

II. VOCABULARY WORDS

besiege

calamity

banquet

coronation

elaborate

III. GRAMMAR REVIEW: CONJUNCTIONS

Conjunctions are words that join words, phrases, and clauses together.

They are easy to remember and recognize when you use the acronym FANBOYS:

For

And

Nor

But

Or

Yet

So

Example:

David loved God **yet** did an evil thing.

Solomon asked for wisdom **but** God gave him riches too.

. Write a sentence for each **conjunction**.

a. For:

b. And:

c. Nor:

d. But:

e. Or:

f. Yet:

g. So:

IV. COMPREHENSION AND MEMORIZATION

2. Answer the following questions.

    a. What does the Bible often refer to the myrtle shrub as?

    b. What story did Nathan, the prophet, tell David to reveal the evil thing David had done?

    c. What happened to David's son, Absalom? Who did the prophet, Nathan, anoint as king when David was very old and frail?

    d. How did Solomon show his wisdom with the two women?

    e. How long did it take Solomon to build the temple?

    f. How long did the people celebrate the completion of the temple?

. If you were Solomon and God asked you what you want from Him and you could have anything, what would you ask God for? Why? How do you think God would respond to your request? Why? Answer the questions below.

V. ACTIVITY

Read about the temple in 1 Kings chapters 5 and 6. Ask your parents to help you find more information about Solomon's Temple. You will need books or to find information online. Try to find pictures of what the temple may have looked like.

Create your own version of Solomon's Temple. You may use any variety of materials such as shoe boxes, clay, craft sticks, markers, paint, crayons, etc. Be sure to make a special room for the ark of the covenant.

Show your finished creation to your family.

VI. GRAMMAR SCHOLARS

There is a type of conjunction called a Correlative Conjunction. They are just like the conjunctions we learned but they use two words.

Correlative Conjunctions:

whether . . . or

either . . . or

neither . . . nor

both . . . and

not only . . . but also

Examples:

God is ***not only*** good ***but also*** patient.

Proverbs says ***either*** to work hard or be poor.

Write a sentence for each conjunction.

a. whether . . . or:

b. either . . . or:

c. neither . . . nor:

d. both . . . and:

e. not only . . . but also:

I. VERSE OF THE WEEK

"And he will give Israel up because of the sins Jeroboam has committed and has caused Israel to commit" (1 Kings 14:16).

II. VOCABULARY WORDS

lavishly

amassed

disgruntled

prophesied

cloak

III. GRAMMAR REVIEW: QUOTATION MARKS

Quotation Marks are used to enclose the exact words said by someone.

Example:

Again Elijah said to Elisha, "Stay here while we go to Jericho."

Notice that when a full sentence is being quoted, a capital letter is used to start the first word of the quotation. The period at the end of the quoted sentence comes before the quotation mark. A comma is used to set off the part of the sentence showing who said something.

1. For the following sentences, place quotations marks in the right place.

   a. At Bethel the resident prophets said to Elisha, Do you realize that God is going to take Elijah away from you soon?

   b. As Elisha saw it, he cried out, My Father! The chariots and horsemen of Israel!

   c. When Elisha reached them, they bowed to him, saying, The spirit of Elijah has come upon you.

2. Practice writing sentences using direct quotes of complete sentences.

   a.

   b.

IV. COMPREHENSION AND MEMORIZATION

3. Answer the following questions.

   a. What queen visited Solomon?

b. What did Solomon give to the queen before she left?

c. What effect did Solomon's foreign wives have on him?

d. How did God react to this? What did Solomon's son, Rehoboam, tell the people he would do to them?

e. How did the people react?

f. What did Elijah do for the widow who gave him food and water?

g. How did the people react when fire engulfed Elijah's altar?

h. Who was Ahab's wicked wife?

i. Who wanted a double portion of Elijah's spirit?

V. ACTIVITY

Draw your own cartoon comic strip using bubbles to show dialogue. Be sure to use complete sentences and proper punctuation and quotation marks in the bubbles.

Show your comic strip to your family.

VI. BIBLE SCHOLARS

Pretend you work as a reporter for a newspaper and write an article recounting one or more of the events in Elijah's life as if you were an eyewitness. Read it to your family.

I. VERSE OF THE WEEK

"Neither before nor after Josiah was there a king like him who turned to the LORD as he did — with all his heart and with all his soul and with all his strength, in accordance with all the Law of Moses" (2 Kings 23:25).

II. VOCABULARY WORDS

mocking

complicated

treachery

defiance

majesty

III. GRAMMAR REVIEW: CAPITALIZATION

Remember to use a **capital letter** to begin the first word of a sentence, name (proper noun), place (country, city, street). Use a **capital letter** for months and days of the week. Also use a capital letter for the word **I**.

Example:

My friend and I are going to Jerusalem in October.

1. Write a sentence using your birthday and the city you were born in. Write another sentence using the word I. Write one more sentence using a day of the week.

   a.

   b.

   c.

IV. COMPREHENSION AND MEMORIZATION

2. Retell the story of Naaman in your own words.

3. Describe what kind of king Josiah was.

V. ACTIVITY

On page 98 is a beautiful Psalm written by David. Choose your favorite section of this Psalm. Selecting at least four lines and using your best handwriting, make a poster to hang up in your room as a reminder to give God your praise.

VI. GRAMMAR SCHOLARS

Pick out a paragraph from a book. Copy it neatly onto a piece of paper. Underline each capital letter.

I. VERSE OF THE WEEK

"If you return to the LORD, then your fellow Israelites and your children will be shown compassion by their captors and will return to this land, for the LORD your God is gracious and compassionate. He will not turn his face from you if you return to him" (2 Chronicles 30:9).

II. VOCABULARY WORDS

allies

plundered

restoration

essential

butler

exile

incensed

III. GRAMMAR REVIEW: SENTENCE TYPES & PUNCTUATION

There are four kinds of sentences:

Declarative — makes a statement and ends with a period

Imperative — gives a command and ends with a period

Interrogative — asks a question and ends with a question mark

Exclamatory — shows excitement and ends with an exclamation point

Examples:

Declarative: Jehoshaphat and the people fell on their knees in thanksgiving.

Imperative: Bring out the book of the Law.

Interrogative: Can I help you?

Exclamatory: Today is God's holy day!

1. State what kind of sentence and add the correct punctuation for each problem.

   a. Long live the king

   b. The joy that God gives makes us strong

   c. Go and have a good meal

   d. Why are the people upset

2. Write four sentences. Write a declarative, imperative, interrogative, and exclamatory sentence.

   a.

b.

c.

d.

IV. COMPREHENSION AND MEMORIZATION

3. Explain the power of praising God.

4. Retell in your own words the life of Joash. What have you learned by reading about his life?

5. Retell in your own words the account of how Jerusalem was rebuilt.

V. ACTIVITY

Write a song or a play using all four types of sentences. Read your song or act out your play to your family.

VI. BIBLE SCHOLARS

After the walls of Jerusalem were rebuilt, what did Ezra do? How did this make the people feel? What did they do about it? Read Matthew 4:4, Luke 11:28, Romans 10:17, and Hebrews 4:12. How important is it in the life of a Christian to read the Bible? How often do you read the Bible? Write out your Bible-reading goals. Ask a parent to help you find a daily Bible-reading plan to help you accomplish your goals. Retell in your own words the account of how Jerusalem was rebuilt. (Hint: parents may want to search the Internet for plans that can be printed.)

. VERSE OF THE WEEK

Your word is a lamp for my feet, a light on my path" (Psalm 119:105).

I. VOCABULARY WORDS

assassinate

conspirator

innocent

circumstances

pastures

II. GRAMMAR REVIEW: INTERJECTIONS

nterjections express surprise or strong emotion. They are usually set apart by an exclamation point or omma. They are usually found at the beginning of a sentence.

Examples:

Wow! Esther was brave.

No, Haman is not a friend of the queen.

. Write four sentences using interjections. Write two using an exclamation point and two using a comma.

a.

b.

c.

d.

V. COMPREHENSION AND MEMORIZATION

. Read Job chapter 40:15–24. Think about what kind of creature God is describing in this passage. Draw a picture of it. (Note to parents or instructor: We highly recommend reading the footnotes in *The Henry Morris Study Bible*.)

3. Read Job 41. What kind of creature do you think God is describing in this chapter? Draw a picture of it. (Note to parents or instructor: We highly recommend reading the footnotes in *The Henry Morris Study Bible*.)

4. Read Job 40:6–14. What do you think God is trying to say to Job? Why do you think God allowed Job to suffer? Discuss your answer with your parents.

5. Write a Psalm to the Lord. Share it with your family.

V. ACTIVITY

Pretend you are celebrating Purim with your family. Read the story of Esther on page 105 before the evening meal. Every time you say Haman's name have your family boo and hiss. While you enjoy your meal, think about the joy the Jewish people felt at being delivered from Haman's evil plan.

VI. BIBLE SCHOLARS

Pick one of your favorite Psalms and memorize it. Recite it to a parent.

. VERSE OF THE WEEK

"But those who hope in the LORD will renew their strength. They will soar on wings like eagles; they will run and not grow weary, they will walk and not be faint" (Isaiah 40:31).

I. VOCABULARY WORDS

distilled

contrasts

fulfilled

sundial

tribute

II. GRAMMAR REVIEW: COMMAS

Commas indicate a pause in a sentence.

Commas are used when three or more items are listed in a series.

Example:

Proverbs gives us instruction, insight, and wisdom.

A meaningful life does not come from treasure, laughter, and song.

Holy, holy, holy is the Lord.

1. Write three sentences listing three or more items, placing commas where they are needed.

   a.

   b.

   c.

Commas are used when writing dates.

Example:

She was born on November 26, 2001.

2. Write two sentences using dates. For the first sentence, use the date you were born. For the second sentence, use the date someone in your family was born.

   a.

   b.

Commas are used when writing an address.

Example:

Sarah Smith

12 Main Street

Green Forest, AR 72638

3. Write your address using a comma in the correct place.

When using a place name in a sentence, use a comma after each item.

Example:

Sarah Smith lives in Green Forest, Arkansas, in a white house.

4. Write a sentence using the name of a city and state.

IV. COMPREHENSION AND MEMORIZATION

5. What does the Book of Proverbs contain?

6. For the writers of Proverbs, what is the key to life and wisdom?

7. Go through the Book of Proverbs and find one that you can work on applying to your life. Write it here and memorize it. Say it to your parents.

8. Read Ecclesiastes 3:1–8. What is the author trying so say? What seasons listed in this passage have you experienced?

9. What did the prophet Isaiah foretell?

V. ACTIVITY

Play a conjunction game with your family. The first person will say a short phrase. The next person will add a conjunction. The next person will finish the sentence with another phrase.

Example:

First person: "I got lost"

Next person: "so"

Last person: "I bought a map"

Continue adding to your story in this order.

VI. GRAMMAR SCHOLARS

An independent clause can stand alone as a complete sentence. A comma is used when joining two independent clauses that are separated by a conjunction. (See Worksheet 12 for lesson on conjunctions.) The comma comes before the conjunction.

Example:

A boil made Hezekiah gravely ill, and he asked the Lord to heal him.

"A boil made Hezekiah gravely ill" is the first independent clause.

"He asked the Lord to heal him" is the second independent clause.

The word "and" is the conjunction. The comma comes before the conjunction.

10. Write three sentences using a comma to join two independent clauses that are separated by a conjunction.

a.

b.

c.

. VERSE OF THE WEEK

This is what the LORD says, he who made the earth, the LORD who formed it and established it — the LORD is his name: 'Call to me and I will answer you and tell you great and unsearchable things you do not know' " (Jeremiah 33:2–3).

I. VOCABULARY WORDS

servant

archaeology

fasting

dungeon

repatriated

II. GRAMMAR REVIEW: IRREGULAR PLURALS

Most **plurals** are formed by adding *s* or *es*. **Irregular Plurals** do not follow this pattern.

Words that end in **fe** add **s**.

Words that end in *f*, change the *f* to *v* and add *es*.

Examples:

knife = knives

half = halves

1. Change each word into a plural word.

    a. life:

    b. loaf:

For words that end in **is**, change the **is** to **es**.

Examples:

crisis = crises

analysis = analyses

2. Change each word into a plural word.

    a. basis:

    b. oasis:

The following words end in **en** when they are plural:

child = child**ren**

man = m**en**

ox = ox**en**

woman = wom**en**

3. Write a sentence for each plural word:
   a. children:

   b. men:

   c. oxen:

   d. women:

The following *oo* words are made plural by changing the *oo* to *ee*:

foot = f**ee**t

goose = g**ee**se

t**oo**th = t**ee**th

4. Write a sentence for each plural word:
   a. feet:

   b. geese:

   c. teeth:

The following *ouse* words are made plural by changing the **ouse** to **ice**:

m**ouse** = m**ice**

louse = **lice**

5. Write a sentence for each plural word:
   a. mice:

   b. lice:

V. COMPREHENSION AND MEMORIZATION

. Read the passage of the suffering servant on page 117. This passage is a prophecy of Jesus. Compare this passage to the life of Jesus. Give at least five ways the life of Jesus fulfilled this prophecy. (You may talk to a parent to help explain the passage and the life of Jesus.)

. Read again the section "God's word cannot be destroyed" on page 120. It was foolish for King Jehoiakim to think he could destroy the word of God. Do you ever forget that what God says in the Bible is true? Do you ever think you can sin and get away with it? Write about a time you forgot that God sees everything. Remember to ask God to forgive you and commit yourself to remembering that God's word is always true.

ACTIVITY

Think about how Jeremiah watched the potter turning clay into a new pot. Think about how God warned the people that if they didn't stop doing evil, He would crush the clay and start over again. We are all like clay in God's hands. He molds and shapes us.

Create a clay pot using modeling dough or clay. Decorate it by carving designs into it using a toothpick. (Please have a parent help you complete this project.)

VI. GRAMMAR SCHOLARS

The following words are spelled the same for both the singular and plural form:

deer

Fish

means

offspring

series

sheep

species

Write a sentence for each plural word:

a. deer:

b. fish:

c. means:

d. offspring:

e. series:

f. sheep:

g. species:

. VERSE OF THE WEEK

"During the night the mystery was revealed to Daniel in a vision. Then Daniel praised the God of heaven and said: 'Praise be to the name of God for ever and ever; wisdom and power are his'" (Daniel 2:19–20).

I. VOCABULARY WORDS

desperately

captives

tormented

cinder

reluctantly

II. GRAMMAR REVIEW: TITLES

When writing a **title** in you need to know when to use *italics* and when to use quotation marks.

When writing **titles**, *italics* are used for whole works. (Use underlining if you are writing something by hand.) You should use italics for the names of books, films, long poems, magazines, musical works such as operas, CDs, and concertos, newspapers, pamphlets, plays, radio and television programs, and works of art.

Use *italics* (or underlining) also for names of ships, trains, and spacecraft, foreign words and phrases, and scientific names of plants and animals.

Quotation marks should be used to name part of a larger work. For instance, when identifying the chapter of a book, you would use quotation marks.

Do not use underling, italics, or quotation marks for Bible references and other religious works or for legal documents.

Examples:

Have you read the book *N is for Noah* by Ken Ham?

There is a great article called "Friendly Viruses" in the *Answers* magazine.

Note the use of both quotation marks and italics in this sentence.

1. Write four of your own sentences using titles you have read, seen, or are interested in. Make sure at least two of your sentences use quotation marks and two of them use italics (or underlining). Your sentences may also use both italics and quotation marks.

    a.

    b.

    c.

    d.

IV. COMPREHENSION AND MEMORIZATION

2. In your own words describe the vision God gave to Ezekiel about the dry bones.

3. Recount what happened when Daniel and his friends remained faithful to God by requesting a diet of only vegetables.

4. Draw a picture of the statue in King Nebuchadnezzar's dream. Draw an arrow to each section and identify what that part of the statue represented.

5. Draw a picture of Shadrach, Meshach, and Abednego in the fiery furnace. Remember to include the fourth person in the furnace with them. Who do you think the fourth person was? Talk about your answer with a parent.

6. Read the section "Worshipping idols" on page 129. Think about the things you sometimes make more important than God. Write a prayer, asking God to forgive you and to help you to always put Him first.

7. Read the section "Courage to obey God" on page 131. Think about a time you had the courage to obey God. Write about your experience.

V. ACTIVITY

God had Ezekiel display, or act out, the message he had for Israel.

Play a game of Bible Charades with your family.

On about 20 note cards, write down names from the Bible. (You may want to include Adam, Eve, Cain, Abel, Jacob, Esau, etc.) You may want to include descriptions of what they did such as "Moses parted the Red Sea."

The first person draws a card and acts out what is written on the card. The first person to guess what is on the card goes next.

See who is the best at guessing what is on the card.

Have fun!

VI. BIBLE SCHOLARS

Make a list of the rulers mentioned in this section on Daniel. Notice how Daniel faithfully served God no matter who ruled the region in which Daniel was held captive.

I. VERSE OF THE WEEK

He has shown you, O mortal, what is good. And what does the LORD require of you? To act justly and to love mercy and to walk humbly with your God" (Micah 6:8).

II. VOCABULARY WORDS

levies

swindle

visions

reconstructing

despise

III. GRAMMAR REVIEW: ROOT WORD, PREFIX, SUFFIX

A **root word** is the main part of the word.

The **prefix** is a word part that is placed before the root word.

The **suffix** is a word part that is placed after the root word.

Examples:

pre**tend**ing

pre- is the **prefix**, tend is the **root word**, -ing is the **suffix**

re**lax**ed

re- is the **prefix**, lax is the **root word**,- ed is the **suffix**

re**build**

re- is the **prefix**, build is the **root word**

flowing

flow is the **root word**, -ing is the **suffix**

1. Look through this week's reading and find more words that have a root along with a prefix and/or a suffix. Find at least five words. After you write them, circle the root word and underline the prefix and/or the suffix.

a.

b.

c.

d.

e.

IV. COMPREHENSION AND MEMORIZATION

2. Summarize in your own words God's message to His people that was given through the prophet Amos.

3. Have you ever become discouraged? The people in Haggai had become discouraged so they gave up on the Lord's work, rebuilding the temple. They focused on building themselves houses but neglected building God's house. God warned them that they needed to do His work but that He would bless them. What do you do when you become discouraged? Do you continue on in your work or do you distract yourself with fun things that only benefit you? What will you do the next time you become discouraged? Write down your plan.

4. What have you learned about what happens when God's people do evil or sin, forget about Him, and stray far from Him? What happens when they return to Him? What do think God does when you sin? What does He do when you say you are sorry and return to Him?

V. ACTIVITY

Draw a comic strip of the story of Jonah. Show it to your family.

VI. GRAMMAR SCHOLARS

Sometimes adding a suffix will change the spelling of the root word. One example is for words ending in a consonant plus "y." The "y" is changed to "i" when adding the suffix.

Stor**my** + er = stormier

hap**py** + ness = happiness

Note: When adding the suffix 'ing' to a word ending in "y" you keep the "y."

copy + ing = cop**y**ing

Add a suffix to the root words and change the spelling as needed. Add –ing to at least one word.

a. fry:

b. lonely:

c. costly:

d. amplify:

e. crunchy:

. VERSE OF THE WEEK

She will give birth to a son, and you are to give him the name Jesus, because he will save his people from heir sins" (Matthew 1:21).

I. VOCABULARY WORDS

testament

gospel

Messiah

ascension

implications

incense

II. GRAMMAR REVIEW: HOMONYMS

Homonyms are words that look alike and sound alike but have different meanings.

Examples:

The word **arm** can mean a part of the body or to provide weapons.

The word **chicken** can mean a type of bird or to be scared.

1. Look up the words and write two definitions for each of the **homonyms**.

   a. can:

   b. check:

   c. fall:

   d. left:

   e. match:

2. Write four sentences using homonyms not listed above.

   a.

   b.

   c.

   d.

IV. COMPREHENSION AND MEMORIZATION

3. Read Luke 1:42–55. Summarize what Elizabeth said.

4. Compare the reactions of Mary and Joseph, and Zechariah and Elizabeth, to the announcements they received. Who of these people do you usually react like when you receive surprising news? Read "Trusting what God says" on page 144. While these couples had angels visit them with big news, we have messages from God that we can trust too. The messages are found in the Bible. Write out your favorite message (verse or verses) from the Bible that you can trust.

V. ACTIVITY

Memorize the books of the Bible. Recite them for your family. Have a sword drill with your family to see how fast you can look up Scripture verses. Have someone call out Scripture references such as "Luke 1:3" and race to see who can find the verse the fastest. When the verse is found, whoever found it the quickest reads the verse.

VI. BIBLE SCHOLARS

Give a summary for each book of the New Testament.

  a. Matthew:

  b. Mark:

  c. Luke:

  d. John:

  e. Acts:

  f. Romans, 1 and 2 Corinthians, Galatians:

  g. Ephesians, Philippians, Colossians, Philemon:

  h. Titus, Timothy:

  i. Hebrews:

  j. James:

  k. 1 Peter:

  l. 2 Peter and Jude:

  m. 1 John:

  n. 2 and 3 John:

  o. Revelation:

I. VERSE OF THE WEEK

Jesus said to him, 'Away from me, Satan! For it is written: "Worship the Lord your God, and serve him only" ' " (Matthew 4:10).

II. VOCABULARY WORDS

possessions

stable

manger

inquiries

implications

Gentiles

III. GRAMMAR REVIEW: COMPOUND WORDS

Compound Words are two words joined together to make a new meaning.

Examples:

The word *life* and the word *time* create a new word **lifetime**.

The word *fire* and the word *fly* create a new word **firefly**.

1. Create your own compound words and use them in a sentence.

   a.

   b.

   c.

   d.

   e.

IV. COMPREHENSION AND MEMORIZATION

2. Describe the surroundings where Jesus was born.

3. Describe in your own words what the angels told the shepherds.

4. How many wise men were there?

5. Who told the wise men to let him know where Jesus was so he could go and worship him too?

6. What three gifts did the wise men give to Jesus?

7. Which two people praised God when they saw the baby Jesus in the temple for His dedication?

8. Who warned Joseph in a dream that King Herod was trying to kill Jesus?

9. Where did Joseph, Mary, and Jesus flee to?

10. When they came back, in what town and region did Jesus and His parents settle?

11. Describe in your own words what happened when Jesus was 12, when His family traveled to Jerusalem for the Passover feast.

12. Who baptized Jesus and what happened?

13. When the devil tempted Jesus in the desert, he tried to use Scripture in a wrong way to trick Jesus. Jesus replied with Scripture used in the right way. Do you ever feel like the devil is trying to trick you into doing something wrong? Think of some Scripture verses you can use to resist him and write them down.

V. ACTIVITY

Play a compound word picture game with your family. One person draws a picture of a compound word. The rest of the family tries to guess what word the picture represents. The person who guesses the right word in the fastest time gets to draw the next picture. Have fun!

VI. BIBLE SCHOLARS

As Christians, Bible events are frequently expressed in our holidays. How does your family include the story of Jesus into your Christmas celebration? Can you think of some new ways to celebrate the birth of Jesus as part of your family's Christmas? (Hint: Use the example of Elizabeth's praise, the wise men's gifts, etc.) Write them down and ask a parent about adding them to your traditions.

I. VERSE OF THE WEEK

The Spirit of the Lord is on me, because he has anointed me to proclaim good news to the poor. He has sent me to proclaim freedom for the prisoners and recovery of sight for the blind, to set the oppressed free, to proclaim the year of the Lord's favor" (Luke 4:18–19).

II. VOCABULARY WORDS

opposition

ordinary

occupation

succession

parable

compromised

interpretation

III. GRAMMAR REVIEW: SYNONYMS

Synonyms are words that mean the same thing. **Synonyms** can be found in a thesaurus. (Ask a parent for a thesaurus to look up synonyms.) When writing a sentence you may want to clarify meaning or make it more interesting but cannot think of the right word. A thesaurus can help you find the right **synonym** of a word you are thinking of.

Examples:

Synonyms of the word *pity*: compassion, mercy, sympathy

Synonyms of the word *pour*: flood, gush, spill

1. Find words in your book that you would like to know **synonyms** for. Write the words you chose, then give at least four **synonyms** for each word. (Use a thesaurus to look up **synonyms**.) Choose one of the four and write a sentence using the **synonym**.

   a.

   b.

   c.

   d.

IV. COMPREHENSION AND MEMORIZATION

2. Whose ministry made the way for Jesus?

3. How old was Jesus when His public ministry began, and about how long did it last?

4. On what were Jesus' teachings firmly based?

5. Why did Jesus criticize the Pharisees?

6. What did Jesus mean when he spoke of the kingdom of God?

7. Where did Jesus' public ministry mostly take place?

8. What was Jesus' first recorded miracle?

9. How did Simon react to the miracle of catching an abundance of fish when he followed Jesus' instructions?

10. Mary told the servants to do whatever Jesus told them to do. Do you think they were nervous about serving the master of the house the liquid that came out of the water jugs? Do you sometimes get nervous obeying God's Word? Write about a time you felt nervous about obeying. What happened when you obeyed?

V. ACTIVITY

Pretend you are going to a party with your family. No one at the party knows your family, so you will need to introduce them. Conduct an interview with one or two family members, asking them to describe themselves. Write down five to ten descriptive words they use. Look up synonyms to replace each descriptive word. Write an introduction for each family member you interviewed, using your new descriptive words. Read your introductions to your family.

VI. BIBLE SCHOLARS

1. Your memory verse this week is the passage Jesus spoke that is a quote from what book of the Bible? Bonus: Ask a parent to help you find the verse Jesus referred to in the Old Testament.

2. Name the twelve Apostles.

a.	e.	i.
b.	f.	j.
c.	g.	k.
d.	h.	l.

I. VERSE OF THE WEEK

"In the same way, let your light shine before others, that they may see your good deeds and glorify your Father in heaven" (Matthew 5:16).

II. VOCABULARY WORDS

paralyzed

denounce

debate

eternal

narrow

III. GRAMMAR REVIEW: ANTONYMS

Antonyms are words that mean the opposite. **Antonyms** can be found in a Thesaurus. **Antonyms** can be helpful in choosing the right word to convey meaning.

Examples:

Antonyms of the word *hot*: cold, arctic, freezing

Antonyms of the word *happy*: sad, miserable, troubled

1. Find words in your book that you would like to know **antonyms** for. Write the word you chose then give at least three **antonyms** for each word. (Use a thesaurus to look up **antonyms**.) Choose one of the four and write a sentence using the **antonyms**.

    a.

    b.

    c.

    d.

IV. COMPREHENSION AND MEMORIZATION

2. After Jesus healed the ten lepers, how many of them came back to thank him?

3. To whom did Jesus say, "I have not found anyone, even in Israel, with so much faith"?

4. What did Jesus say to the paralyzed man that angered some of the religious leaders?

5. Why did Jesus criticize the Pharisees?

6. What two things did Jesus do on the Sabbath that angered the religious leaders?

7. What kind of water did Jesus tell the woman at the well that he could give to her?

V. ACTIVITY

Find a short story book to read out loud to your family. As you read the story, pick out words and replace them with antonyms. Let family members take turns reading a page, replacing words with their antonyms. See how silly it makes the story sound, and have fun!

VI. BIBLE SCHOLARS

Read Matthew 5:3–11 and complete the Beatitudes

    a. Blessed are

    b. Blessed are

    c. Blessed are

    d. Blessed are

    e. Blessed are

    f. Blessed are

    g. Blessed are

    h. Blessed are

    i. Blessed are

I. VERSE OF THE WEEK

"Therefore everyone who hears these words of mine and puts them into practice is like a wise man who built his house on the rock" (Matthew 7:24).

II. VOCABULARY WORDS

sensible

command

confessed

sneered

indignant

cunning

III. GRAMMAR REVIEW: SIMILES

A **simile** is a phrase that compares two things using the words like or as. **Similes** can make writing come alive. We have used well known **similes** for examples to help show what they are, but be careful not to add overly used **similes** to your writing. Be creative and come up with new **similes**.

Examples:

blind *as* a bat

eats *like* a pig

1. Write four sentences using similes. Write two sentences using the word *as* and two sentences using the word *like*.

   a.

   b.

   c.

   d.

IV. COMPREHENSION AND MEMORIZATION

2. Explain how you can build your life on the rock.

3. When the storms of life crash in on us, we can trust Jesus. Tell about a time when you were scared. Did you turn to God and trust Him? What happened?

4. Jesus performed many miraculous healings including the woman who touched Him. He also raised people from the dead, including Jairus' daughter. Do you think you could trust Jesus more if you saw Him do a miracle? Read John 20:29. What does it say about people who have believed without seeing?

5. Why was Jesus so angry at the merchants in the temple?

6. What temple did Jesus rebuild in three days?

7. Think about traveling throughout your state to share the good news of Jesus. What would you say to people? Would you be willing to go if you knew people would hate you and maybe even try to kill you? Missionaries and evangelists often do this work, but we all can share the gospel. Make a plan to share the gospel with someone you know. Be sure to bring along a friend and ask a parent for permission first.

V. ACTIVITY

Write a story using at least seven **similes**. Draw a picture of at least two of your **similes**. Read your story and show your pictures to your family.

VI. BIBLE SCHOLARS

What does "born again" mean? Making sure you are born again is the most important thing you can do in your life. If you are not born again, talk to a parent about becoming born again.

I. VERSE OF THE WEEK

"This, then, is how you should pray: 'Our Father in heaven, hallowed be your name, your kingdom come, your will be done, on earth as it is in heaven. Give us today our daily bread. And forgive us our debts, as we also have forgiven our debtors. And lead us not into temptation, but deliver us from the evil one' " (Matthew 6:9–13, the Lord's Prayer).

II. VOCABULARY WORDS

impress

blunt

criticized

secluded

dispersed

distress

III. GRAMMAR REVIEW: METAPHORS

A **metaphor** is a like a simile except it does not use the words *like* or *as* when making a comparison between two unlike things. **Metaphors** make writing interesting and can help paint a picture of what the writer is trying to say. They usually make a stronger statement than a simile.

Examples:

He is a night owl.

He has a heart of stone.

1. Go back to the four sentences you wrote in Worksheet 25 using similes. Change them into **metaphors**.

   a.

   b.

   c.

   d.

IV. COMPREHENSION AND MEMORIZATION

2. Explain in your own words the parable of the sower.

3. Who tricked King Herod into killing John the Baptist?

4. How much food was left over after Jesus fed the crowd with two small fish and five loaves of barley bread?

5. Who walked on water when Jesus called him out of the boat? If you were one of the disciples and Jesus called you out onto the water, do you think you would have faith enough to do it? Can you think of ways sometimes God asks us to walk on water (or to do something impossible)? When Peter started to walk on the water, he became distracted and fearful of the wind and the waves. Do you ever become fearful of situations going on around you? What did Jesus do to help Peter? How can you reach out and grab Jesus' hand when you are afraid?

6. What message is Jesus giving to Gentiles in the final story you read this week about the woman and her demon-possessed daughter? What does this mean for you?

V. ACTIVITY

Find five of your favorite things. Write a poem about them using metaphors to describe why you like them. Share your poem with your family.

VI. BIBLE SCHOLARS

Jesus often spoke in parables. Ask a parent to help you to research Jesus' parables. Find out how many parables there are. Bonus: list them. (Note: You may want to use helps found in a Bible or the Internet. Some parables are found in more than one book of the Bible.)

I. VERSE OF THE WEEK

'I am the good shepherd. The good shepherd lays down his life for the sheep" (John 10:11).

II. VOCABULARY WORDS

glorified

destined

battered

extravagant

undeterred

dubious

famine

III. GRAMMAR REVIEW: DOUBLE NEGATIVES

A **double negative** phrase uses two negative words such as no, not, none, etc., and should not be used. A double negative phrase expresses a positive, which is usually the opposite of what is trying to be said. **Double negatives** cause confusion and are improper.

Examples:

I do **not** have **no** oatmeal.

To not have no oatmeal means you have oatmeal.

A better way to express this is to change one of the negatives into a positive:

I do not have any oatmeal.

Or simply remove one of the negatives:

I have no oatmeal.

1. Re-write each sentence, correcting the double negatives.

    a. Do not tell no one about the transfiguration of Jesus.

    b. A priest came by and acted like he did not see nothing.

    c. Why is that you are not wearing no wedding clothes?

IV. COMPREHENSION AND MEMORIZATION

2. Jesus asked His disciples, "Who do people say that I am?" He then asked, "Who do you say that I am?" Peter answered saying, "You are the Messiah, the Son of the living God." What would say if you were asked who Jesus is?

3. Describe in your own words what happened when Jesus was glorified (transfigured).

4. Retell in your own words the parable of the Good Samaritan. Explain what it means.

5. Explain what the parable of the great wedding feast means.

6. How are the parables of the lost coin and the prodigal son similar?

7. Describe in your own words how Jesus describes Himself as the good shepherd.

V. ACTIVITY

Write a letter as if you are the father of the prodigal son, asking him to come home and sharing how you feel about him. Then take something that is important to you (ask a parent first!) and hide it. Read the letter to your family, explaining that this is how God feels about all people. Then have your family go search for the item you hid. You may need to give clues, but remind everyone that God keeps seeking to find every lost person. Rejoice together when the item is found.

VI. GRAMMAR SCHOLARS

Re-write each sentence, correcting the **double negatives**.

a. The Pharisees believed that Jesus should not mix with no tax collectors.

b. I have worked hard for years without causing you none trouble.

c. No one can force me to not do it.

I. VERSE OF THE WEEK

'Jesus said, 'Let the little children come to me, and do not hinder them, for the kingdom of heaven belongs to such as these' " (Matthew 19:14).

II. VOCABULARY WORDS

objected

perfection

grant

resurrection

humble

III. GRAMMAR REVIEW: RUN-ON SENTENCES

A **run-on sentence** is when two independent clauses (complete sentences) are used together without the correct punctuation.

Example:

Run-on sentence:

Five girls were foolish they took no extra oil to light their lamps.

A **run-on sentence** can be fixed in several ways. Here are two of them.

A. It can be changed into two separate sentences.

Example:

Five girls were foolish. They took no extra oil to light their lamps.

B. When the two sentences are closely related, they can be separated by a semi-colon.

Example:

Five girls were foolish; they took no extra oil to light their lamps.

1. Re-write each sentence, correcting the **run-on sentences**. Identify which method you used to fix the sentences by indicating A or B. Be sure to use both methods.

a. Give all that you have you will have treasure in heaven.

b. Lazarus is dead he will rise once more.

IV. COMPREHENSION AND MEMORIZATION

2. What have you learned about the kinds of people that Jesus welcomed to Himself?

3. What couldn't the young man give up to follow Jesus? What did Jesus say would be a reward for people who give up family or possessions?

4. Retell in your own words the account of Lazarus. How would you have felt if you were there when he was raised from the dead? Would you have been excited, scared, or maybe both? What would you have thought about Jesus? Imagine being with Lazarus after this experience and having someone threaten to kill him. What do you think Lazarus would say?

5. Why did Jesus accept the prayer of the tax collector and not the Pharisee?

5. What did Zacchaeus decide to do after his meeting with Jesus?

7. Retell the parable of the workers to a parent. Ask them about the saying, "The first will become last and the last will become first." What does this saying mean?

8. Why was the small gift of the widow worth more to Jesus than great sums of money given by others?

V. ACTIVITY

Create a poster with both a picture and description for the items that need to be italicized or underlined. For example, draw a book and write "names of books" under your picture. Hang your poster up to remind you which titles need italics.

VI. GRAMMAR SCHOLARS

Remember, a **run-on sentence** is when two independent clauses (complete sentences) are used together without the correct punctuation.

We already covered two ways a **run-on sentence** can be fixed.

A. It can be changed into two separate sentences.

B. When the two sentences are closely related, they can be separated by a semi-colon.

There are two more ways a **run-on sentence** can be fixed.

C. A run-on sentence can also be corrected by using a comma and (coordinating) conjunction such as *and, but, for, nor, or, so, yet*

Example:

Five girls were foolish, as they took no extra oil to light their lamps.

D. A **run-on sentence** can be corrected by placing a (subordinating) conjunction before one of the independent clauses (sentences), including as, as though, *as long as , although, because , before, even though, except that, in order that, just as, since , so that, though, when, whereas , while*

Example:

Five girls were foolish because they took no extra oil to light their lamps.

Re-write each sentence, correcting the **run-on sentences**. Identify which method you used to fix the sentences by indicating C or D. Be sure to use both methods.

a. Have mercy on me I am nothing but a wicked sinner.

b. I will give away half of what I own to the poor I will repay four times what I have taken dishonestly.

Re-write the sentence, correcting the **run-on sentences**. You may use any of the four methods. Identify which method you used by indicating A, B, C, or D.

c. Those who are last will become first those who are first will become last.

I. VERSE OF THE WEEK

"Then the King will say to those on his right, 'Come, you who are blessed by my Father; take your inheritance, the kingdom prepared for you since the creation of the world' " (Matthew 25:34).

II. VOCABULARY WORDS

bridegroom

ruthless

Hosanna

magnificent

betray

III. GRAMMAR REVIEW: SENTENCE COMBINING

Sentence combining is the art of changing many short, choppy sentences into longer, more effective ones. There are many ways to **combine sentences**, so the object is to find the most effective way to combine them.

Examples:

We need to combine the following short, choppy sentences.

There were ten girls waiting for a wedding feast.

Five girls were foolish.

Five girls were wise.

Five girls did not bring extra oil for their lamps.

Five girls brought extra oil for their lamps.

We can combine the sentences in different ways. Let's try a few. Think about which one is most effective.

- There were ten girls waiting for a wedding feast; five of them brought enough oil for their lamps but five of them did not.

- There were ten girls waiting for a wedding feast. The five wise girls brought extra oil for their lamps but the five foolish girls did not.

- Out of ten girls waiting for a wedding feast, only five girls brought enough oil for their lamps.

Which of these sentences do you think is most effective for telling the parable?

Let's try some more. Remember to think about which one is most effective.

The foolish girls complained.

The foolish girls asked the wise girls for oil.

The wise girls said no.

The wise girls said there may not be enough oil to share.

The wise girls said to quickly go buy more oil.

- The foolish girls complained and asked the wise girls for more oil but they said there may not be enough so quickly go buy more.

- The foolish girls complained and asked the wise girls for more oil. The wise girls explained that there may not be enough and sent them to go buy more.

- Even though the foolish girls complained and asked for more oil, the wise girls told them to go buy more since there may not be enough.

Which of these sentences do you think is most effective for telling the parable?

Let's try one more set of sentences to finish the parable.

The bridegroom arrived.

The wise girls went to the wedding feast.

The foolish girls were locked out.

- The bridegroom arrived, taking the wise girls to the wedding feast. He locked out the foolish girls.

- When the bridegroom arrived the wise girls went to the wedding feast but the foolish girls were locked out.

- The wise girls went to the wedding feast when the bridegroom arrived; however, the foolish girls were locked out.

Which of these sentences do you think is most effective for telling the parable?

1. Take the sentences you thought were most effective and write them out in a paragraph to summarize the parable. Read your paragraph. Does it tell the parable in the most effective way? If your parable would sound better, try replacing one of the sentences with another one.

V. COMPREHENSION AND MEMORIZATION

2. What is the moral (meaning) of "the wise and foolish girls" parable?

3. In the parable of 'the talents,' why was the master angry with the servant that hid the money? What did he do to the servant? What talents has the Lord given to you to use for Him?

4. Retell in your own words the parable of the sheep and the goats. What does the parable mean? You may want to discuss the meaning of the parable with a parent.

5. Jesus rode into Jerusalem on a donkey. What was the donkey a symbol of?

6. When will Jesus be ready to return?

7. What did Jesus teach the Disciples when he washed their feet?

8. What biblical holiday did Jesus and the Disciples celebrate at the last supper? What does your church call the celebration of the last supper? What represents the body of Jesus that was broken for us? What represents the blood Jesus shed to forgive our sins? Be sure to talk to a parent about the meaning of communion if you do not fully understand it.

V. ACTIVITY

In the parable of the sheep and the goats, Jesus talks about giving the thirsty a drink, welcoming a stranger, giving clothes to those in need, caring for the sick, and visiting those in prison. He says when we do these things for others, we do them for Him. You may not think you can do any of those things but you can. Make a card for someone you know who is sick. You may need a parent to help you send or give the card to the person. Remember, it is like giving the card to Jesus when you give it to someone who is sick.

VI. GRAMMAR SCHOLARS

1. Give three ways to combine the following sentences. You may use more than one sentence if needed.

A man went on a long journey.

Before the man left he summoned his servants.

The man put his servants in charge of a sum of money.

He gave the first servant five talents.

He gave the second servant two talents.

He gave the third servant one talent.

a.

b.

c.

2. Give three ways to combine the following sentences. You may use more than one sentence if needed.

The first servant made another five talents.

The second servant made another two talents.

The third servant hid his talent.

The third servant dug a hole in the ground.

The third servant hid the talent in the ground.

The third servant left the talent in the ground.

a.

b.

c.

I. VERSE OF THE WEEK

"I am the vine; you are the branches. If you remain in me and I in you, you will bear much fruit; apart from me you can do nothing" (John 15:5).

II. VOCABULARY WORDS

inspired

courtyard

evidence

riot

III. GRAMMAR REVIEW: OXYMORON

An **oxymoron** is a figure of speech where two opposite words are joined together to create a unique effect. An **oxymoron** adds interest to writing because it is both true and false at the same time.

Examples:

He was *sadly happy*.

It was *old news*.

A *small crowd* gathered.

Dinner is *almost ready*.

The dog is *awfully good*.

He took his *bird dog* hunting.

When you look at the words in the sentences, you see that two of the words are opposite or not alike at all. Sadly is the opposite of happy. Small is the opposite of crowd.

1. Have some fun creating sentences with an oxymoron.

   a.

   b.

   c.

   d.

IV. COMPREHENSION AND MEMORIZATION

2. How did Jesus prepare His Disciples for His death? How does His message encourage you to live?

3. How did Judas betray Jesus in the garden?

4. Who cut the ear off one of the high priest's servants? What did Jesus do?

5. Who was the high priest who asked Jesus if He was the Christ, the Son of God? How did Jesus respond? How did the high priest react?

6. Retell the account in your own words of when Peter disowned Jesus. How would you have felt if you were Peter?

7. What did Pontius Pilate think of Jesus? Why did he turn Jesus over to the soldiers to crucify Him? Why did Pilate publicly wash his hands?

8. What did the soldiers do to mock Jesus? Who did the soldiers force to carry the cross when Jesus couldn't? What did they do with Jesus' clothes?

9. What prayer did Jesus say regarding His murderers? What were the last words He spoke? What happened when He died? What did that show?

10. Who asked Pilate for Jesus' body and placed it in a tomb he had cut out of rock for himself? What was rolled in front of the tomb's entrance after Jesus was placed in it?

V. ACTIVITY

Find a newspaper article that interests you. Re-write the article, inserting as many oxymoron expressions as you can. Use at least five, but try to think of even more. Ask your family to take turns reading your article. See who can identify all of the oxymoron expressions.

VI. BIBLE SCHOLARS

Jesus died for all of our sins. How does the crucifixion of Jesus make you feel? How do you think His Disciples felt? Talk to a parent about what you have read about the crucifixion. Ask questions about anything you do not understand and write the answers down here.

I. VERSE OF THE WEEK

"Then Jesus told him, 'Because you have seen me, you have believed; blessed are those who have not seen and yet have believed' " (John 20:29).

II. VOCABULARY WORDS

dominated

vanished

solemn

commotion

III. GRAMMAR REVIEW: HYPERBOLE

Hyperbole (hahy-pur-buh-lee) is a figure of speech that uses exaggeration for emphasis, effect, or impact.

Hyperbole is not meant to be interpreted literally. It is used in poetry and creative writing, but should be avoiding in formal writing.

Examples:

The stone was heavier than the moon.

Jesus appeared to His Disciples millions of times before returning to heaven.

The pancakes he made for breakfast were stacked up a mile high.

They were so afraid they shook until there was an earthquake.

The earthquake cracked the entire earth in half.

1. Have some fun creating sentences using hyberbole.

    a.

    b.

    c.

    d.

IV. COMPREHENSION AND MEMORIZATION

2. Why did the women go to Jesus' tomb early in the morning? What were they told?

3. What did Mary think happened to Jesus' body?

4. Why do people call someone who is a skeptic a "doubting Thomas"?

5. Why do you think Jesus repeatedly asked Peter if he loved Him? What do you think He meant by Jesus' instructions to Peter to feed His lambs, look after His sheep, and feed His sheep? Is this something people should do today? (Note: If you are not sure what any of this means, talk to a parent.)

6. What kind of kingdom did Jesus come to build? How will Jesus return one day?

7. What feast were the Jews celebrating when the Holy Spirit came upon the Christians? Describe in your own words what happened that day.

V. ACTIVITY

Did you know that the Feast of Pentecost, a biblical feast celebrated by Jews for many years, was a feast of anticipation? They were to count down 50 days from Passover in anticipation of Pentecost. Pentecost was a harvest festival, where they were thankful for the first of the summer harvest.

Do you think the disciples thought 50 days was a long time to wait for a holiday, a time to be joyful, after the crucifixion and Resurrection of Jesus? Do you think they knew they would receive the gift Jesus promised, the Holy Spirit, on the Day of Pentecost? When the Holy Spirit came, they also began to receive a harvest, a harvest of new Christians.

With the help of your family, plan a special day. Write down what you will do and what you will eat together. Set up a calendar where you can cross off the days for a whole week in anticipation of your special day. While you are waiting in anticipation, think about how the Jews did this every year and how God revealed a very special part of His plan on the Day of Pentecost. When your special day arrives, enjoy it with your family and thank God for all of the good things He gives to us, including the gift of His Holy Spirit.

VI. BIBLE SCHOLARS

Think about all of the events we have learned about, starting from the crucifixion of Jesus and ending with the baptism of the Holy Spirit. How does this affect our faith? Can you explain how the crucifixion replaced the need to sacrifice animals for our sin? How does this change our relationship with God? (Note: Please discuss what you have learned with a parent and ask any questions you may have.)

I. VERSE OF THE WEEK

"Peter replied, 'Repent and be baptized, every one of you, in the name of Jesus Christ for the forgiveness of your sins. And you will receive the gift of the Holy Spirit'" (Acts 2:38).

II. VOCABULARY WORDS

commissioned

persecute

extensively

gifted

III. GRAMMAR REVIEW: PARAGRAPHS

A **paragraph** has three parts — the topic sentence, supporting sentences, and a closing sentence.

Read this sentence from your book, and identify the three parts of the paragraph.

When at last they spied land, the ship hit a sandbank and was smashed to pieces. The soldiers wanted to kill all the prisoners in case they escaped, but Julius stopped them because he wanted to save Paul. All 276 people reached the shore and were saved, just as God had promised.

The first sentence is the **topic sentence**. It is what the paragraph is about.

The second sentence is the **supporting sentence**. It provides details about the topic.

The last sentence is the **closing sentence**. It completes the topic and lets the reader know the paragraph is complete.

Go to page 223 of your book and see if you can identify the **topic sentence**, **supporting sentence**, and **closing sentence** of more paragraphs. (Hint: when a new paragraph begins, the first line is indented.)

1. Choose a paragraph from your book and write it here. Be sure to indent the first line of the paragraph. Underline the topic sentence and closing sentence.

2. A paragraph should have a theme. It should be about one topic. In this paragraph, cross out the sentence that does not belong.

The early Christians shared the love of Jesus with many people. Some traveled as missionaries to foreign countries. Some were forced to move because of persecution. Some, like Paul, were shipwrecked on islands. They brought people food. Regardless of how they got to new places, they shared the good news of the gospel wherever they went.

IV. COMPREHENSION AND MEMORIZATION

3. Fill in the blank with the correct name.

    Aeneas, Ananias, Barnabas, Peter, Philip, Sapphira, Tabitha

    a. "Son of encouragement" _____

    b. Healed after being paralyzed for eight years _____

    c. Raised from the dead after Peter prayed _____

    d. The apostle who said "I have neither gold nor silver" and went on to heal a beggar _____

    e. The man who died after lying about money _____

    f. The woman who also died after lying about money _____

    g. The apostle who explained the gospel to the Ethiopian and baptized him _____

4. Retell the story of Saul's conversion in your own words.

5. Why do you think Jesus chose Paul to reveal Himself to in order to spread the gospel even though Paul was guilty of persecuting the Christians? Have you ever had someone be mean to you when you have not done anything to him or her? Let the story of Paul encourage you to pray for that person. You never know, God could reveal Himself to that person and he or she may change. We never know what God may have planned. Write a prayer to God for the person who has mistreated you, that like Paul, he or she might have a change of heart and repent. Continue to keep that person in your prayers.

V. ACTIVITY

Write your own paragraph. You can use an idea from your book or use a topic that interests you. Remember to indent the first line. Your paragraph must have a topic sentence, one or more supporting sentences, and a closing sentence. Your paragraph must have a central idea, topic, or theme. Use your best handwriting. Ask a parent to read your paragraph.

VI. GRAMMAR SCHOLARS

Write a short story using two or three paragraphs. Follow the rules for writing paragraphs. You may retell a story in your book in your own words or you may choose your own topic. Use your best handwriting. Have a parent read your story.

I. VERSE OF THE WEEK

"For since the creation of the world God's invisible qualities — his eternal power and divine nature — have been clearly seen, being understood from what has been made, so that people are without excuse" (Romans 1:20).

II. VOCABULARY WORDS

nationality

ancient

intervening

acclaimed

magistrates

flogged

caravan

III. GRAMMAR REVIEW: TYPES OF WRITING: NARRATIVE

A **narrative** is a type of writing that tells a story from one person's point of view. The story can be true or not true. A true story is called nonfiction. A story that is not true is called fiction. A narrative can be imaginative, about your own life, or about another person's life. It is meant to entertain the reader, but a **narrative** should have a point, lesson, or moral to the story. It should include plenty of sensory-related detail such as descriptions of sights, sounds, and smells.

There is some structure with **narrative** writing:

Setting — when and where the story takes place

Characters — including the main character and the other people in the story

Problem or challenge the main character faces

Events — what happens as the main character works to solve the problem

Resolution — how the problem is resolved

Example:

The woman opened her front door and cautiously peered out into the night. She listened carefully for a repeat of the noise she had heard coming from the driveway. She scanned the neighborhood but everyone was tucked safely inside their homes. Only an occasional stray cat and passing car broke the silence of the night. She anxiously stepped out into the cool night air to get a better view of her minivan parked in the driveway. At that moment she wished she had replaced the burned-out bulb in her porch light. Suddenly, she heard a yelp. As she jumped back in surprise, a strong, acrid odor filled her nose. Two beady eyes pleaded with her as they leaped toward the door, which she quickly shut behind her!

1. Finish the narrative essay from the example. Remember to include the point of the story in your resolution. Also include plenty of sensory-related detail such as descriptions of sights, sounds, and smells.

2. From the example narrative essay you finished, identify the following:
   a. Setting
   b. Characters
   c. The problem
   d. Events
   e. Resolution (including the point, or moral, of the story)

IV. COMPREHENSION AND MEMORIZATION

3. Describe the dream Peter had, and tell what it meant.

4. What did Rhoda forget to do when Peter came to the door after the earthquake freed him from prison?

5. What happened to Bar-Jesus, the false prophet, because he was opposing the work of the Lord being done by Paul and Barnabas? What happened because of this?

5. Retell in your own words the account of when the earthquake struck the prison Paul and Silas were in.

7. Think about all the times Paul was beaten, in prison, and shipwrecked yet nothing would stop him from sharing the gospel message. He was even prepared to die for the sake of Christ. We too must be prepared to live for Jesus. Even though you may not be beaten or shipwrecked or have to go to prison, you still can live for Jesus. Tell how you live your life for Him.

8. What was Paul trying to teach the new believers in Rome through his letter?

9. What was Paul trying to teach the believers in Ephesus through his letter?

V. ACTIVITY

Create a play out of the narrative essay you finished. You take the lead role, but if you need help acting out other characters, enlist the help of your family. After you have practiced the play, gather your family together for a fun performance.

VI. GRAMMAR SCHOLARS

Write your own fictional narrative essay. Remember to include the setting, characters, problem, events, and resolution. Read your essay to your family.

I. VERSE OF THE WEEK

"But you are a chosen people, a royal priesthood, a holy nation, God's special possession, that you may declare the praises of him who called you out of darkness into his wonderful light" (1 Peter 2:9).

II. VOCABULARY WORDS

interpreting

pure

mature

splendor

III. GRAMMAR REVIEW: TYPES OF WRITING: NARRATIVE

Let's review what a narrative is. A **narrative** is a type of writing that tells a story from one person's point of view. The story can be true or not true. A true story is called non-fiction. A story that is not true is called fiction. A narrative can be imaginative, about your own life, or about another person's life. It is meant to entertain the reader, but a narrative should have a point, lesson, or moral to the story. It should include plenty of sensory-related detail such as descriptions of sights, sounds, and smells.

There is some structure with **narrative** writing:

Setting — when and where the story takes place

Characters — including the main character and the other people in the story

Problem or challenge the main character faces

Events — what happens as the main character works to solve the problem

Resolution — how the problem is resolved

Remember, a **narrative** can be imaginative, about your own life, or about another person's life. We created an imaginative **narrative** in our previous lesson. For this lesson we are going to focus on the other two kinds of **narratives**: biography and autobiography. A **biography** is a **narrative** about someone else. An **autobiography** is a **narrative** about your own life. Whether you create an imaginative, biography, or autobiography narrative, it needs to include the five elements of structure.

The **narrative** in the previous lesson was an imaginative **narrative** since it was completely made up. An **autobiography narrative** is a true story about the author's life. A **biography narrative** is a true story of another person.

Here is an example of a biography narrative. It is a true story.

One day my son decided to make brownies. He got out a bowl, a spoon, and all of the ingredients to make them. He preheated the oven to the exact temperature specified in the recipe. He carefully measured the dry ingredients and added them to the bowl before mixing in the wet ingredients. The batter was a perfect creamy blend of brown goodness just waiting to be baked to perfection. As my son poured the mixture into the pan, he could hardly wait to eat a warm, gooey brownie. As he slid the pan into the oven, his stomach began to growl.

Soon, the sweet smell of chocolate filled the house. Little feet and big feet began to appear, wondering when the delicious brownies would be ready. Our son sent all of the spectators away, assuring them he would summon all once the brownies were fully cooked and cooled. They dejectedly walked away, only to come scrambling back when a loud sound pierced the air, announcing all was not well with the contents of the oven. Our son ran to the stove as smoke rose. He quickly opened the oven door, causing a loud gasp to escape from the onlookers. The once perfect brownie goodness was growing! As it grew, it spilled over the edges of the glass pan, filling the bottom of the oven where it was scorched into unrecognizable shapes of stinky, sticky goo.

Once the smoke detectors were silenced and the mess was cleaned away, a group of dejected mouths began to question what went wrong. The oven was quickly cleared of all wrongdoing. The recipe seemed to be the correct concoction to produce beautiful, edible brownies. All fingers pointed to baker error. Unless you want to try a fantastic but very messy experiment, do not make the mistake of confusing a tablespoon from a teaspoon when measuring baking powder in a brownie recipe!

1. Name the three types of narratives.

   a.

   b.

   c.

   Which type is a story about yourself?

   d.

2. Name the five elements of structure that must be included in a narrative.

   a.

   b.

   c.

   d.

   e.

IV. COMPREHENSION AND MEMORIZATION

3. How is the church like a human body?

4. How did Paul respond when he heard that some of the Christians in Corinth claimed there was no life after death?

5. What was Paul's advice for Christians waiting for the Second Coming of Jesus?

6. Give examples of at least three people from the Old Testament and how they were examples of faith. You may find the examples on page 230 of your book or by reading Hebrews 11.

7. Describe in your own words John's vision of heaven. Who will join Jesus in heaven? Discuss with a parent why it is important to share the gospel with unbelievers.

V. ACTIVITY

Paul wrote many letters to people. He wrote letters to missionaries and church leaders, instructing and encouraging them. Write an encouraging letter to a missionary. If possible, find a missionary to send your letter to. Ask a parent for help.

Peter wrote letters to encourage people who are persecuted for their faith. There are many people today who are persecuted for their faith. Write an encouraging letter to someone who is being persecuted for their faith. If possible, find a missionary to send your letter to. Ask a parent for help.

VI. GRAMMAR SCHOLARS

Ask a parent to help you choose a biography. It can be a short or a long book. Read the book. What did you like about the biography? Write a short summary of the biography using at least two paragraphs.

Write either a biography or an autobiography narrative essay. If you decide to do a biography, you may need to interview family members for a story you can tell. Remember to include the setting, characters, the problem, events, and the resolution. Also include plenty of sensory-related details such as descriptions of sights, sounds, and smells. Read your essay to your family.

I. GRAMMAR REVIEW: TYPES OF WRITING: DESCRIPTIVE

A **descriptive** paragraph describes a person, place, or thing in such detail the reader can vividly see, hear, and experience it in his or her mind. The reader should be able to personally relate to the subject of the paragraph.

Here is an example of a descriptive paragraph.

The farmers in Israel grow some of the most amazing grapes. As the harvest approaches, a sweet haze of a fruity aroma lingers in the fields. The green leaves of the vines are tangled together like a neglected girl's hair. In between the mass mess of leaves dangles the tempting clusters of glistening purple globes. Row after row invites every passerby to reach in and pick a sweet, juicy treat. As the farmer begins to pick load after load of his beautiful grapes, the whole community anticipates running a sweet liquid over their tongues to quench their thirst. It is an exciting time to be in Israel as the grape harvest begins.

Did you notice the simile used in the descriptive paragraph? Similes and metaphors are frequently used in descriptive paragraphs.

1. Pick a topic found in your book covered in this week's lesson such as a nomad's way of life, going to synagogue, camels, or Nazareth. Write a descriptive paragraph about the topic you chose. Remember, readers should feel like they are seeing, hearing, tasting, or experiencing the topic you wrote about. Be sure you indent the first line of your paragraph. Also be sure your paragraph has a topic sentence, supporting sentences, and a closing sentence. You may want to use a simile or a metaphor to help describe your topic.

II. COMPREHENSION AND MEMORIZATION

2. Describe nomads.

3. Describe the homes the Israelites lived in when they settled in Canaan.

4. Describe farming for the Israelites in the land of Cannaan.

5. Describe the typical diet of the Israelites, including forbidden foods.

6. If you were a young Jewish boy or girl growing up in the time of Jesus, in the region of Galilee, describe what life would have been like for you. Describe what activities you may have participated in, such as synagogue or school.

7. Describe the Sabbath.

8. Tell when each Jewish feast or festival is held and what it is about.
   a. Rosh Hashanah

   b. Yom Kippur

   c. Succoth

   d. Hanukkah

   e. Purim

   f. The Passover

   g. Shavuot

). Describe the plants mentioned in Bible times.

10. Describe the domestic animals mentioned in Bible times.

11. Describe the wild animals mentioned in Bible times.

12. Where was Jesus born? Where did He grow up?

13. Describe the following bodies of water.

    a. The Sea of Galilee

    b. The river Jordan

    c. The Dead Sea

14. Describe the Judean wilderness.

III. ACTIVITY

Pretend you own a travel agency and you are trying to sell a trip to Israel. Write a letter to your customers using descriptive paragraphs to convince them to visit Israel. You may use the sample paragraph and the paragraph you already wrote, but you must write at least one or two new paragraphs. (If you choose to use the two paragraphs already written, you may want to make some changes to them to read more like an advertisement for a trip.) Read your letter to your family, and see if they are ready to travel to Israel!

I. COMPREHENSION AND MEMORIZATION

1. Identify the Bible's connection to each place.

   a. Ur:

   b. Egypt:

   c. Sinai:

   d. Babylon:

   e. Damascus:

   f. Rome:

   g. Corinth, Thessalonica, and Philippi:

   h. Athens:

   i. Ephesus

2. The list of people found in the Bible on pages 246–247 are listed in alphabetical order. Re-write the names here in the order they appear **by name** in the Bible. (Note: You may need your Bible.) The names are listed here so that you can cross them off as you put them into the correct order. You may find clues by reading the descriptions in your book. (Note: The order found in the Bible is not always the exact order of when they lived in history.) The Old Testament people will be easier than the New Testament. (Hint: Do not go by the names and order of the books in the New Testament!) You may need a parent's help and a good concordance or searchable digital Bible to complete the New Testament names.

Aaron, Abraham, Adam,

Daniel, David, Deborah,

Elijah, Elisha, Esau, Esther, Eve, Ezekiel Ezra,

Gideon, Hannah, Isaac, Isaiah,

Jacob, James (brother of Jesus), James (son of Zebedee), Jeremiah, Jesus, Job, John (the apostle), John the Baptist, Joseph (husband of Mary), Joseph (son of Jacob), Joshua, Judas Iscariot,

Luke, Mark, Mary (mother of Jesus), Matthew, Moses,

Nehemiah, Noah,

Paul, Peter, Pontius Pilate, Ruth,

Samson, Samuel, Sarah, Saul, Solomon,

Thomas, Timothy, Zacchaeus

II. ACTIVITY

Create a timeline using the information found on pages 244–245 of your book. If there are events you would like to use and you are not certain of the exact date, insert them where you think they belong

Elementary Bible and English Grammar

Quizzes

1. Write a definition for each of the following words. (4 Points Each)

   salvation

   famine

   Exodus

   prophet

2. Write a short description of each of the genres used in the Old Testament. (4 Points Each)

   a. The Law:_____.

   b. History:_____.

   c. Poetry:_____.

   d. Prophecy:_____.

3. Underline the common nouns and circle the proper nouns in the following sentences: (4 Points Each)

   a. The Bible is a collection of many books of different kinds of writing.

   b. The Bible has one central message: God's salvation of His people.

4. Underline the main verbs in the following sentences: (4 Points Each)

   a. God appeared to Abraham in a vision.

   b. Abraham trembled before God.

5. Circle the helping verbs in the following sentences: (4 Points Each)

   a. I will give this land to you and your many descendants.

   b. Jacob was amazed that God had spoken to him.

6. What do we call the Passover feast we celebrate today? (4 Points)

7. Give an adjective to describe each noun: (4 Points Each)
   a. Moses:

   b. snake:

8. Write out the two commandments Jesus says all of the laws are based on. (4 Points Each)
   a.

   b.

9. Underline the adverb in each sentence. (4 Points Each)
   a. Moses, you will soon die.

   b. Slowly he climbed Mount Nebo.

10. Identify the correct person for each description. (4 Points Each)
   a. Pulled down the altar to Baal _____

   b. The man who married Ruth _____

11. For each sentence, underline the prepositional phrase if it has one. (4 Points Each)
   a. Ruth stayed by Naomi's side.

   b. Ruth set the grain down.

1. Write a definition for each of the following words. (4 Points Each)

   anoint

   gratitude

   prophesied

   exile

2. Answer the questions. (4 Point Each Blank — 20 Points Total)

   a. What name did Hannah give to the baby that she promised to consecrate to the Lord, and what does that name mean? _____ _____

   b. Who were the first three kings of Israel? _____, _____, _____

3. Was having a king a good thing for Israel? (4 Points)

4. Combine the two words to create a contraction. (4 Points Each)

   a. That is

   b. We are

5. Answer the questions. (4 Points Each)

   a. What did Goliath rely on in the battle?

   b. What did David rely on in the battle?

   c. What city did David make the capital of Israel?

6. Place quotations marks in the right place. (4 Points Each)

   a. At Bethel the resident prophets said to Elisha, Do you realize that God is going to take Elijah away from you soon?

   b. As Elisha saw it, he cried out, My Father! The chariots and horsemen of Israel!

7. Answer the following questions. (4 Points Each)

   a. What effect did Solomon's foreign wives have on him?

   b. Who was Ahab's wicked wife?

   c. Who wanted a double portion of Elijah's spirit?

8. Write a sentence using your birthday and the city you were born in. (4 Points)

9. Explain the power of praising God. (4 Points)

10. Write your address using a comma in the correct place. (4 Points)

11. What does the Book of Proverbs contain? (4 Points)

12. According to the Book of Proverbs, what is the key to life and wisdom? (4 Points)

13. What did the prophet Isaiah foretell? (4 Points)

14. Change the words into a plural word. (4 Points Each)

   a. life:

   b. loaf:

1. Write a definition for each of the following words. (4 Points Each — 16 Points Total)

   gospel

   Gentile

   parable

   eternal

2. Recount what happened when Daniel and his friends remained faithful to God by requesting a diet of only vegetables. (4 Points)

3. Add a suffix to the root words and change the spelling as needed. (4 Points Each)

   a. fry:

   b. lonely:

   c. costly:

   d. amplify:

   e. crunchy:

4. Give two definitions for each homonym. (4 Points Each)

   a. can:

   b. fall:

5. How many wise men were there? (4 Points)

6. What three gifts did the wise men give to Jesus? (4 Points Each)

7. Who baptized Jesus and what happened? (4 Points)

8. On what was Jesus' teachings firmly based? (4 Points)

9. What was Jesus first recorded miracle? (4 Points)

10. After Jesus healed the ten lepers, how many of them came back to thank Him? (4 Points)

11. What two things did Jesus do on the Sabbath that angered the religious leaders? (4 Points)

12. Explain how you can build your life on the rock. (4 Points)

13. What temple did Jesus rebuild in three days? (4 Points)

14. How much food was left over after Jesus fed the crowd with two small fish and five loaves of barley bread? (4 Points)

15. Re-write each sentence, correcting the double negatives. (4 Points Each)
    a. Do not tell no one about the transfiguration of Jesus.

    b. A priest came by and acted like he did not see nothing.

16. Retell in your own words the parable of the Good Samaritan. (4 Points)

1. Write a definition for each of the following words. (4 Points Each — 16 Points Total)

   resurrection

   inspired

   persecute

   ancient

2. Re-write run-on sentence: Give all that you have you will have treasure in heaven. (4 Points)

3. Jesus rode into Jerusalem on a donkey. What was the donkey a symbol of? (4 Points)

4. When will Jesus be ready to return? (4 Points)

5. Who cut the ear off one of the high priest's servants? What did Jesus do? (4 Points)

6. What prayer did Jesus say regarding His murderers? What were the last words He spoke? What happened when He died? What did that show? (4 Points)

7. What kind of kingdom did Jesus come to build? How will Jesus return one day? (4 Points)

8. Fill in the blank with the correct name. (4 Points Each)
   Aeneas, Ananias, Barnabas, Peter, Philip, Sapphira, Tabitha
   a. "Son of encouragement" _____
   b. Healed after being paralyzed for eight years _____
   c. Raised from the dead after Peter prayed _____
   d. The apostle who said "I have neither gold nor silver" and went on to heal a beggar _____
   e. The man who died after lying about money _____
   f. The woman who also died after lying about money _____
   g. The apostle who explained the gospel to the Ethiopian and baptized him _____

9. What did Rhoda forget to do when Peter came to the door after the earthquake freed him from prison? (4 Points)

10. Name the five elements of structure that must be included in a narrative. (4 Points Each)

a.

b.

c.

d.

e.

11. How is the Church like a human body? (4 Points)

12. What was Paul's advice for Christians waiting for the Second Coming of Jesus? (4 Points)

Elementary Bible and English Grammar

Test Your Knowledge

OLD TESTAMENT

1. What were the names of the first human beings that God made?

2. Who was Isaac's father?

3. Who got transformed into a pillar of salt as she looked back?

4. Who was thrown into prison, had dreams, but eventually became prime minister of Egypt?

5. Who led the Israelites through the Red Sea?

6. Which woman protected the spies at the city of Jericho?

7. What was the name of Ruth's mother-in-law?

8. What was the name of the priest that Samuel served under?

9. What was the name of David's closest friend?

10. Who is particularly famous for his wisdom?

11. Who was the prophet who followed Elijah?

12. What was the name of the seven-year-old boy who was crowned King of Israel?

13. Who is particularly famous for his suffering and patience?

14. Who was thrown in the lion's den?

1. What was the name of John the Baptist's father?

2. What were the three gifts the Magi (wise men) brought to Jesus?

3. In which town did Mary and Joseph live?

4. Where was the wedding at which Jesus changed the water into wine?

5. For how much did Judas betray Jesus?

6. What was the occupation of Simon Peter?

7. In which city was Straight Street?

8. What kind of tree did Zacchaeus climb to see Jesus?

9. What does the name "Peter" mean?

10. What was the name of the wife of Herod Antipas?

11. What was the name of the man to whom Jesus said, "You must be born again"?

12. What was written over Jesus' cross at the crucifixion?

13. Where was Phillip going when he met the Ethiopian official?

14. How old was Jesus when Mary and Joseph found Him teaching in the temple?

15. What is the name of the festival at which Christians remember the coming of the Holy Spirit?

16. On which island in the Mediterranean Sea did Paul safely land after being shipwrecked?

GENERAL

1. By what other name is Mount Sinai known?

2. Where did Elijah's contest with the priests of Baal take place?

3. What musical instruments did the people play as they went round the city of Jericho?

4. What was poured over Saul's head when he was made king?

5. What was the name of the town near Jerusalem where Jesus was born?

6. On the road to which city was Paul going when he was blinded by the light of Jesus?

7. In which city was the famous temple of Artemis?

8. Who was swallowed by a great fish?

9. What does "gospel" mean?

10. How many books does the Bible contain?

11. Which Roman emperor is famous for his persecution of the Christians?

1. Which bird, representing the Holy Spirit, came upon Jesus at His baptism?

2. What kind of animal, belonging to Balaam, spoke God's words?

3. When Moses threw his staff on the ground, which creature did it turn into?

4. Jesus said that Peter would disown him three times before he heard the sound of which bird?

5. The valuable crop of which tree is used for making oil?

6. What birds did Joseph and Mary bring as a sacrifice when they presented Jesus in the temple?

7. Which bird fed Elijah?

8. On which mountain range did Noah's boat come to rest after the flood?

9. Beside which lake were Simon and Andrew catching fish when Jesus invited them to catch people?

10. In which river did John the Baptist baptize Jesus?

11. Which creature does the prophet Joel use as a warning of God's judgment?

Answer Keys

for

Elementary Bible and English Grammar

Worksheet 1

Pentateuch (the first five books of the Bible)

descendant (a person whose heritage can be traced to a particular individual or group)

integrity (the quality of having a strong moral character)

genre (a category of literature, music, or art that is similar in style or subject matter)

testament (evidence or proof that something is true)

1. a. The Law
   b. History
   c. Poetry
   d. Prophecy

2. a. History
   b. Letters
   c. Prophecy

3. a. **The Law:** These books describe the origin of the Jewish people and culture.
   b. **History:** These books describe the historical accounts of the Israelites.
   c. **Poetry:** These books deal with important questions of life.
   d. **Prophecy:** In these books prophets predicted future events, especially about the coming Messiah.

4. See page 9 of textbook.

The Old Testament

The Law: Genesis, Exodus, Leviticus, Numbers, Deuteronomy

History: Joshua, Judges, Ruth, 1 Samuel, 2 Samuel, 1 Kings, 2 Kings, 1 Chronicles, 2 Chronicles, Ezra, Nehemiah, Esther

Poetry: Job, Psalms, Proverbs, Ecclesiastes, Song of Songs

Prophecy: Isaiah, Jeremiah, Lamentations, Ezekiel, Daniel, Hosea, Joel, Amos, Obadiah, Jonah, Micah, Habbakkuk, Zephaniah, Haggai, Zechariah, Malachi

The New Testament

History: Matthew, Mark, Luke, John, Acts

Letters: Romans, 1 Corinthians, 2 Corinthians, Galatians, Ephesians, Philippians, Colossians, 1 Thessalonians, 2 Thessalonians, 1 Timothy, 2 Timothy, Titus, Philemon, Hebrews, James, 1 Peter, 2 Peter, 1 John, 2 John, 3 John, Jude

Prophecy: Revelation

5. Answers will vary.

VI. Answers will vary.

Worksheet 2

biblia (Greek word for Bible)

prophetic vision (the act or ability to see future events before they happen)

salvation (being saved from the power and penalty of sin)

paradise (a place of incredible beauty and happiness)

cunning (shrewd or tricky)

1. a. The Bible is a collection of many books of different kinds of writing.
   b. The Bible has one central message: God's salvation of His people.
   c. God made a beautiful *garden* called Eden, a paradise full of animals and fruit trees.

2. a. god (Answers will vary.)
   b. garden (Answers will vary.)
   c. woman (Answers will vary.)
   d. prophet (Answers will vary.)
   e. book (Answers will vary.)
   f. country (Answers will vary.)
   g. day (Answers will vary.)

3. Answers will vary.
4. Answers will vary.
V. Answers will vary.
VI. Answers will vary.

Worksheet 3

nomad (a person or tribe of people that have no permanent home but move from place to place)

adze (a tool similar to an axe used for cutting large pieces of wood)

chisel (a tool with a cutting edge used for shaping or carving wood or stone)

gangway (an opening in a ship with a moveable bridge-like structure that serves as a passageway)

sophisticated (an idea, machine, or person that has been developed or educated to a high degree)

1. a. God appeared to Abraham in a vision.
   b. Abraham trembled before God.

c. Sarah <u>treated</u> Hagar unkindly.

d. God <u>sent</u> angels to <u>destroy</u> the city.

2. a. located

b. Run

c. pulled

d. gathered

e. believed

f. transformed

3. Answers will vary.

4. Answers will vary.

5. Answers will vary.

VI. Answers will vary.

Worksheet 4

sacrifice (to surrender or destroy something valuable for the sake of something or someone else)

inheritance (money, property, or possessions that pass from the owner upon death to an heir)

cunning (deceptive or sly)

lentil (a member of the pea family)

agreement (a contract or arrangement that is agreed upon by all parties)

1. a. I (will) give this land to you and your many descendants.

b. Jacob (was) amazed that God had spoken to him.

c. I (have) seen God face to face and am still alive!

d. I (am) trusting that God will provide a sacrifice.

e. Sarah (had been) listening to their conversation.

2. a. was

b. would

c. did

3. Helping verbs,
Helping verbs,
There are 23,
Am is are was and were
Being been and be
Have has had,
Do does did
Shall will should and would
There are five more helping verbs
May might must can could

4. Answers will vary.

V. Answers will vary.

VI. a. Answers will vary.

b. Answers will vary.

c. Answers will vary.

d. Answers will vary.

e. Answers will vary.

f. Answers will vary.

Worksheet 5

flocks (a herd of animals of one kind)

calamity (a great hardship or misfortune)

signet (official mark or stamp)

famine (a shortage of food in a particular region)

sieve (a device with small holes in the bottom used to separate coarse and fine particles or to strain liquids)

1. a. <u>Joseph</u> (had an unusual dream.)

b. <u>Joseph's brothers</u> (were jealous of him.)

c. <u>The Ishmaelite traders</u> (sold Joseph as a slave.)

d. <u>Our father</u> (has already

lost Joseph.)

e. <u>The Egyptian people</u> (were in danger of starving.)

2. a. Answers will vary.

b. Answers will vary.

c. Answers will vary.

d. Answers will vary.

e. Answers will vary.

3. a. Answers will vary.

b. Answers will vary.

c. Answers will vary.

d. Answers will vary.

e. Answers will vary.

4. Answers will vary.

VI. a. Answers will vary.

b. Answers will vary.

c. Answers will vary.

d. Answers will vary.

e. Answers will vary.

Worksheet 6

overrule (to decide or rule against)

headdress (decorative head covering)

pharaoh (a title given to ancient Egyptian kings)

exodus (a departure of a large number or people)

plague (widespread disease)

1. a. he

b. them

c. they

d. it

e. their

2. a. Answers will vary.

b. Answers will vary.

c. Answers will vary.

d. Answers will vary.

e. Answers will vary.

3. a. The river Nile turned to blood

b. frogs

c. gnats

d. flies

e. a mysterious disease

f. boils

g. hail

h. locusts

i. darkness

j. death of the first born

4. the gods of Egypt

5. Communion

6. Answers will vary.

V. Answers will vary.

VI. Answers will vary.

Worksheet 7

ordination (the act of setting apart or appointing)

scrolls (writings on paper or parchment formed into a roll)

festival (a holy day set apart to worship and celebrate)

rebel (disobedient)

1. a. Answers will vary.

b. Answers will vary.

c. Answers will vary.

d. Answers will vary.

e. Answers will vary.

2. a. Answers will vary.

b. Answers will vary.

3. a. You are to have no other gods before me.

b. Do not try to represent God by making an idol or any other image of Him.

c. Do not misuse the name of the Lord your God.

d. Remember the Sabbath day by keeping it holy.

e. Respect your father and mother.

f. Do not murder.

g. Do not commit adultery.

h. Do not steal.

i. Do not tell lies.

j. Do not long to have anything that belongs to another person.

4. a. Thou shalt love the Lord thy God with all thy heart, and with all thy soul, and with all thy mind.

b. Thou shalt love thy neighbor as thyself.

5. Answers will vary

VI. a. Answers will vary.

b. Answers will vary.

c. Answers will vary.

Worksheet 8

commission (to send out, empower, authorize)

prophet (one instructed by God to speak in His name)

scarlet (a deep, bright red color)

inhabitants (people who live in a town)

allocated (distributed, assigned, or given out)

judgment (punishment from God)

1. a. soon

b. Slowly

c. certainly

d. silently

e. easily

2. Answers will vary.

3. a. Asher

b. Benjamin

c. Dan

d. Gad

e. Issachar

f. Judah

g. Naphtali

h. Reuben

i. Simeon

j. Zebulun

k. Ephraim

l. Manasseh

4. Jacob's ten sons and Joseph's two sons.

5. Answers will vary.

VI. a. – j. Answers will vary.

Worksheet 9

oppression (hardship, cruelty, injustice)

insignificant (meaningless, not important, without value)

summoned (called to appear)

lair (resting place)

gleaning (gathering a crop following the reapers)

1. a. Answers will vary.

b. Answers will vary.

c. Answers will vary.

d. Answers will vary.

e. Answers will vary.

2. a. Answers will vary.

b. Answers will vary.

c. Answers will vary.

d. Answers will vary.

e. Answers will vary.

3. a. Samson

b. Ehud

c. Naomi

d. Gideon

e. Samson

f. Boaz

g. Debrorah

h. Gideons

4. Answers will vary.

VI. a. Ruth stayed <u>by Naomi's side</u>.

b. Ruth set the grain down.

c. Ruth slept <u>near Boaz's feet</u>.

d. Boaz held up his shoe.

e. Boaz took <u>off his shoe</u>.

Worksheet 10

synagogue (a gathering together)

rabbi (teacher)

Bar Mitzvah (son of the commandment)

anoint (to apply oil to set them apart for sacred use)

covenant (an agreement)

1. a. Answers will vary.

b. Answers will vary.

c. Answers will vary.

2. a. Answers will vary.

b. Answers will vary.

c. Answers will vary.

d. Answers will vary.

3. a. Hannah

b. Samuel, heard by God

c. A seven-branched lampstand made of pure gold. The cups are shaped like almond blossoms. It symbolized the glory of the Lord reflected in His people

d. Eli's sons behaved in a wicked way and Eli did nothing to stop them.

e. The statue fell over twice and the second time it broke into pieces.

f. Saul, David, Solomon

g. Saul disobeyed. He made the sacrifice himself instead of waiting for Samuel.

4. They insisted on having a king.

5. 42

6. Eight — Asa, Jehoshaphat, Joash (mostly good), Amaziah (mostly good), Uzziah/Azariah, Jotham, Hezekiah, Josiah

7. Answers will vary, but in most cases having a king was not good and did not help the people serve God better.

8. " 'For my thoughts are not your thoughts, neither are your ways my ways,' declares the LORD. 'As the heavens are higher than the earth, so are my ways higher than your ways and my thoughts than your thoughts.' "

9. Answers will vary.

10. Answers will vary.

VI. a. Answers will vary.

b. Answers will vary.

c. Answers will vary.

Worksheet 11

regretted (very sorry for; feeling bad about something you did or did not do)

jealous (envious or hostile toward a rival)

treacherously (to betray a trust; dangerously unfaithful; falsely)

obscurity (unknown; forgotten)

gratitude (thankful; grateful; appreciation)

1. a. That's

b. We're

c. Shouldn't

d. We'd

e. They've

2. a. Answers will vary.

b. Answers will vary.

c. Answers will vary.

3. a. seven

b. David, the youngest

c. almost ten feet tall

d. Answers will vary but probably between five and six feet tall.

e. His weapons

f. God

g. Saul was jealous.

h. Nabal, He died

i. Nabal's wife, Abigail

j. Jerusalem

k. Joab

l. David, David's son

m. Mephibosheth

4. Answers will vary

VI. Answers will vary

Worksheet 12

besiege (enclose, shut up, on every side, fortify, confine)

calamity (ruin, destruction)

banquet (feast, elaborate meal)

coronation (a ceremony where the crown is put upon the king)

elaborate (detailed, complicated, sophisticated, fancy, expand)

1. a. Answers will vary.

b. Answers will vary.

c. Answers will vary.

d. Answers will vary.

e. Answers will vary.

f. Answers will vary.

g. Answers will vary.

2. a. a symbol of God's generosity

b. A very rich man was entertaining a friend. Although he had many animals, he helped himself to the only lamb of a poor man, killed it, and gives it to his guests to eat.

c. His hair trapped him in an oak tree. Joab killed him.

d. David and Bathsheba's son, Solomon

e. He knew the real mother would not let the baby be cut in half.

f. seven years

g. two weeks

3. Answers will vary.

VI. a. Answers will vary.

b. Answers will vary.

c. Answers will vary.

d. Answers will vary.

e. Answers will vary.

Worksheet 13

lavishly (in a generous way; richly; luxuriously)

amassed (gathered, collected)

disgruntled (unhappy, angry, discontented)

prophesied (predict that something will happen in the future, foretell)

cloak (a loose outer garment that

serves as an overcoat)

1. a. At Bethel the resident prophets said to Elisha, "Do you realize that God is going to take Elijah away from you soon?"

b. As Elisha saw it, he cried out, "My Father! The chariots and horsemen of Israel!"

c. When Elisha reached them, they bowed to him, saying, "The spirit of Elijah has come upon you."

2. a. Answers will vary.

b. Answers will vary.

3. a. Queen of Sheba

b. Everything she asked for.

c. They turned his heart away from God.

d. He would take all but one tribe away from Solomon's son. Make them work harder and beat them with scorpions.

e. They rebelled and proclaimed Jeroboam king, leaving only the tribe of Judah to Rehoboam.

f. Elijah raised her son to life.

g. They cried out, "The Lord is God!"

h. Jezebel

i. Elisha

VI. Answers will vary.

Worksheet 14

mocking (laughing at or making fun in a cruel way, ridicule, treat with contempt)

complicated (intricate, difficult to understand, having many parts or

steps, elaborate)

treachery (betrayal, deceptive, violating a trust, backstabbing)

defiance (refusal to obey, willful, obstinate, resist, oppose, fight)

majesty (royal status, stateliness, grandeur, kingliness, gloriousness, splendor)

1. a. Answers will vary.

b. Answers will vary.

c. Answers will vary.

2. Answers will vary.

3. Answers will vary.

VI. Answers will vary.

Worksheet 15

allies (friends, a person or group that cooperates with each other for a common purpose)

plundered (steal, loot, rob)

restoration (a return of something)

essential (extremely important, absolutely necessary)

butler (a slave that served drinks to the king)

exile (a person forced to leave his or her country)

incensed (angered, furious, livid)

1. a. Exclamatory (Long live the king!)

b. Declarative (The joy that God gives makes us strong.)

c. Imperative (Go and have a good meal.)

d. Interrogative (Why are the people upset?)

2. a. Answers will vary.

b. Answers will vary.

c. Answers will vary.

d. Answers will vary.

3. Answers will vary. See page 99.

4. Answers will vary.

5. Answers will vary.

VI. Answers will vary

Worksheet 16

assassinate (to murder in a surprise attack)

conspirator (someone involved in a secret plan to do harm)

innocent (not guilty, blameless)

circumstances (conditions, surroundings, environment)

pastures (land used for grazing animals)

1. a. Answers will vary.
   b. Answers will vary.
   c. Answers will vary.
   d. Answers will vary.

2. Answers will vary.

3. Answers will vary.

4. Answers will vary.

5. Answers will vary.

VI. Answers will vary.

Worksheet 17

distilled (purify, condense, reduce, refine)

contrasts (compare, notable differences, strikingly unlike in comparison)

fulfilled (satisfied, content, completed, to come to an end)

sundial (the earliest timekeeping device that relies on shadows from the sun to indicate the time of day)

tribute (tax, money given to a ruler)

1. a. Answers will vary.

b. Answers will vary.

c. Answers will vary.

2. a. Answers will vary.
   b. Answers will vary.

3. Answers will vary.

4. Answers will vary.

5. A collection of wise sayings about the best way to live.

6. a God-centered life

7. Answers will vary.

8. Answers will vary.

9. The destruction of Israel by the Assyrians

10. a. Answers will vary.
    b. Answers will vary.
    c. Answers will vary.

Worksheet 18

servant (slave, person hired to perform household work, steward)

archaeology (the branch of science that studies materials such as tools, bones, artifacts, monuments, etc., to understand previous cultures and their activities)

fasting (to go without eating)

dungeon (dark, underground prison)

repatriated (returned to an original country of citizenship)

1. a. lives
   b. loaves

2. a. bases
   b. oases

3. a. Answers will vary.
   b. Answers will vary.
   c. Answers will vary.
   d. Answers will vary.

4. a. Answers will vary.

b. Answers will vary.

c. Answers will vary.

5. a. Answers will vary.
   b. Answers will vary.

6. Answers will vary.

7. Answers will vary.

VI. a. Answers will vary.
    b. Answers will vary.
    c. Answers will vary.
    d. Answers will vary.
    e. Answers will vary.
    f. Answers will vary.
    g. Answers will vary.

Worksheet 19

desperately (almost beyond hope, extremely, intensely)

captives (enslaved, held prisoner,)

tormented (afflicted, suffering greatly, agony, physical or mental pain)

cinder (ember, small piece of burned coal, ashes, charred material, lava fragments)

reluctantly (unwilling, resistant, not eager, opposing)

1. a. Answers will vary.
   b. Answers will vary.
   c. Answers will vary.
   d. Answers will vary.

2. Answers will vary.

3. Answers will vary but may include: They were fitter and healthier than the Israelites who had eaten the royal food.

4. gold head — Nebuchadnezzar's mighty kingdom, other parts — other less great kingdom, the rock — God's eternal kingdom

5. Answers will vary.

6. Answers will vary.

7. Answers will vary.

VI. King Nebuchadnezzar, King Belshazzar, King Darius

Worksheet 20

levies (tax by force, seize)

swindle (scheme, defraud, cheat, deceive)

visions (events seen in the mind that are given by God)

reconstructing (rebuild)

despise (detest, hate, scorn, loathe)

1. a. Answers will vary.

   b. Answers will vary.

   c. Answers will vary.

   d. Answers will vary.

   e. Answers will vary.

2. Answers will vary.

3. Answers will vary.

4. Answers will vary.

VI. a. Answers will vary — check for spelling.

   b. Answers will vary — check for spelling.

   c. Answers will vary — check for spelling.

   d. Answers will vary — check for spelling.

   e. Answers will vary — check for spelling.

Worksheet 21

testament (a covenant between God and His people, binding agreement)

gospel (good news)

Messiah (the anointed one, deliverer, Savior of a captive people, Jesus)

ascension (the act of rising)

implications (possible future effects or results)

incense (material that creates a fragrant aroma when burned)

1. a. able to; metal container usually shaped like a cylinder

   b. look at carefully; a written order instructing a bank to pay out money from a specific account

   c. to drop down quickly; a season, autumn

   d. the position of being on the same side as your heart; go away, depart

   e. equal or similar; a short, thin piece of material treated to light on fire with friction

2. a. Answers will vary.

   b. Answers will vary.

   c. Answers will vary.

   d. Answers will vary.

3. Answers will vary.

4. Answers will vary.

VI. a. **Matthew**: (shows an interest in Jewish Christians: Jesus is the Messiah long expected by the Jews)

   b. **Mark**: (a brief account of Jesus' life and work)

   c. **Luke**: (Luke emphasizes Jesus as Savior of all different kinds of people, especially the poor and needy.)

   d. **John**: (seven signs or miracles and seven saying point to Jesus as the Son of God)

   e. **Acts**: (Takes the story on from Jesus' ascension into heaven, the gift of the Holy Spirit at Pentecost, and the birth of the church. Peter, and later Paul, became leaders, and the message of Jesus spread rapidly from Jerusalem throughout the eastern Roman Empire.)

   f. **Romans, 1 and 2 Corinthians, Galatians**: (emphasize the nature of the gospel preached by Paul)

   g. **Ephesians, Philippians, Colossians, Philemon**: (All written while Paul was a prisoner in Rome, contain teaching on what it means to be a Christian. Paul's letters to the Thessalonians were probably his earliest letters and are especially concerned about Christ's Second Coming.)

   h. **Titus, Timothy**: (contain practical advice on church organization)

   i. **Hebrews**: (shows that Jesus was better than the priesthood and system of sacrifices, and the perfect fulfillment of all that they had stood for)

   j. **James**: (a letter about practical Christianity)

   k. **1 Peter**: (a letter to Christians who were persecuted for their faith)

   l. **2 Peter, Jude**: (warn against false teachers)

   m. **1 John**: (written to help Christians be sure of their faith)

n. **2 and 3 John**: (show some of the implications of the life of love and truth)

o. **Revelation**: (The final book, a prophetic book of visions and symbols, written when Christians were being persecuted. Its author is believed to be John. It opens with a vision of Christ in glory; then come letters to seven churches. Visions of judgment and victory follow, showing God's sovereignty and his triumph over evil. The book ends with a picture of a new heaven and a new earth.)

Worksheet 22

possessions (personal property owned)

stable (a building used to feed and lodge animals; barn)

manger (food trough where food for animals is placed)

inquiries (questioning; the act of seeking information)

implications (possible future effects or results)

Gentiles (a person who is not Jewish; a heathen or pagan, a nonbeliever)

1. a. Answers will vary.
   b. Answers will vary.
   c. Answers will vary.
   d. Answers will vary.
   e. Answers will vary.
2. Answers will vary, but should reflect a humble stable.
3. Answers will vary, but should include telling them not to be afraid and that the Savior has been born.

4. We do not know but it is often assumed three because there were three gifts.
5. King Herod
6. gold, frankincense, myrrh
7. Simeon and Anna
8. an angel
9. Egypt
10. in the town of Nazareth in the region of Galilee
11. Answers will vary but should include Jesus teaching in the temple.
12. John the Baptist; the Holy Spirit came upon Jesus like a dove and a voice cried out from heaven, "This is my own dear Son and I am very pleased with Him."
13. Answers will vary.

VI. Answers will vary.

Worksheet 23

opposition (hostility; against; resistance)

ordinary (common, not special, normal, typical)

occupation (taking possession of a place, seizure, controlling an area)

succession (inheriting a title or position; following in order)

parable (a short story intended to teach a moral or spiritual truth)

compromised (gave something up; weakened; a change for the worse)

interpretation (explanation; a particular version)

1. a. Answers will vary.
   b. Answers will vary.
   c. Answers will vary.
   d. Answers will vary.
2. John the Baptist

3. 30 years, 3 years
4. the Old Testament
5. They distorted the original intent of God's law and made it a heavy burden for the people.
6. God's reign, God's rule in the human heart
7. in the Galilee area of Palestine
8. turning water into wine at a wedding at Cana in Galilee
9. He fell on his knees and cried, "Don't come near me, Lord, I am a sinful person."
10. Answers will vary.

VI. 1. Isaiah 61:1
    2. In any order: Simon Peter, Andrew, James-son of Zebedee, John, Philip, Bartholomew, Matthew, Thomas, James-son of Alphaeus, Simon the Zealot, Judas-son of James, Judas Iscariot

Worksheet 24

paralyzed (unable to move, crippled, disabled)

denounce (condemn; attack; inform against)

debate (argue, discuss, consider)

eternal (forever, undying, infinite)

narrow (slim, slender, skinny, limited in size, thin)

1. a. Answers will vary.
   b. Answers will vary.
   c. Answers will vary.
   d. Answers will vary.
2. one
3. the centurion soldier
4. that his sins were forgiven
5. They distorted the original intent of God's law and made

it a heavy burden for the people.

6. picked corn and ate it, healed people

7. living water

VI. a. Blessed are the poor in spirit, for theirs is the kingdom of heaven.

b. Blessed are those who mourn, for they will be comforted.

c. Blessed are the meek, for they will inherit the earth.

d. Blessed are those who hunger and thirst for righteousness, for they will be filled.

e. Blessed are the merciful, for they will be shown mercy.

f. Blessed are the pure in heart, for they will see God.

g. Blessed are the peacemakers, for they will be called children of God.

h. Blessed are those who are persecuted because of righteousness, for theirs is the kingdom of heaven.

i. Blessed are you when people insult you, persecute you, and falsely say all kinds of evil against you because of Me.

Worksheet 25

sensible (reasonable, responsible, wise)

command (demand, direct, require, issue orders, and order given with authority)

confessed (admit, declare, acknowledge)

sneered (facial expression showing dislike, scorn, or lack of respect)

indignant (displeased, resentful, annoyed, angry)

cunning (crafty, using keen insight, clever)

1. a. Answers will vary.
   b. Answers will vary.
   c. Answers will vary.
   d. Answers will vary.

2. Answers will vary.

3. Answers will vary.

4. Answers will vary. They are blessed.

5. They turned God's house into a common marketplace.

6. his own body

7. Answers will vary.

VI. Answers will vary but should include the concept of trusting in Jesus, being born of the Spirit of God.

Worksheet 26

impress (persuade, influence to look favorably upon)

blunt (abrupt, direct or to the point, frank)

criticized (find fault with, unfavorable judgment, disapproval)

secluded (hidden; solitary, private)

dispersed (distribute, go in different directions, scatter widely)

distress (anxiety, sorrow, pain)

1. a. Answers will vary.
   b. Answers will vary.
   c. Answers will vary.
   d. Answers will vary.

2. Answers will vary.

3. Herodias, Herod's wife, and her daughter Salome

4. twelve baskets

5. Peter, answers will vary

6. Answers will vary, but should include that Jesus cares about Gentiles.

VI. There are 32 parables:

The weeds

The treasure

The pearl

The fishing net

The workers in the harvest

The loaned money

The ten virgins

The two sons

The wedding feast

The unforgiving servant

The wheat

The traveling owner of the house

The noble man's servants

The servant's role

The friend at midnight

The unjust judge

The good Samaritan

The wedding feast

The proud Pharisee and the corrupt tax collector

The rich fool

The great feast

The shrewd manager

The lost coin

The lost son

The forgiven debts

The unproductive fig tree

The yeast

The lost sheep

The wise and faithful servants

The soils

The mustard seed

The wicked tenants

Worksheet 27

glorified (elevated, bestowed honor, magnified, exalted, light up brilliantly)

destined (determined beforehand, dedicated in advance, set apart for a particular purpose)

battered (beat, bruised, repeatedly attacked, bombard)

extravagant (expensive, lavish, exceeding reasonable bounds, not sparing, bountiful)

undeterred (resolute, not discouraged, determined)

dubious (suspicious, untrustworthy, unreliable, questionable, shady)

famine (extreme shortage of food)

1. a. Do not tell anyone about the transfiguration of Jesus.

   b. A priest came by and acted like he did not see anything.

   c. Why is that you are not wearing wedding clothes?

2. Answers will vary.

3. Answers will vary.

4. Answers will vary.

5. Answers will vary.

6. Answers will vary, but should include that God rejoices when a lost sinner is found.

7. Answers will vary, but should be based on the passage found in John 10 and on page 184 of the book.

VI. a. The Pharisees believed that Jesus should not mix with tax collectors.

   b. I have worked hard for years without causing you any trouble.

   c. No one can force me to do it.

Worksheet 28

objected (disagreed, opposed, protested)

perfection (flawless, cannot be improved, supreme excellence)

grant (consent, allow, permit)

resurrection (rising from the dead, a dead person coming back to life)

humble (not proud, modest, meek, not thinking of yourself as better than other people)

1. a. Answers will vary but need to follow one of the two methods of fixing a run-on sentence. The method used should be indicated by A or B.

   b. Answers will vary but need to follow one of the two methods of fixing a run-on sentence. The method used should be indicated by A or B.

2. Answers will vary, but should include the idea that Jesus welcomed all kinds of people, whether rich or poor, sinners, children, etc.

3. his riches, they will receive a hundred times as much as they gave up

4. Answers will vary.

5. Answers will vary, but should include the idea that the tax collector was humble and knew he was a sinner but the Pharisee was proud.

6. He would give away half of what he owned to the poor and repay four times anything he had taken dishonestly.

7. Answers will vary. We encourage parents to take an active role in discussing some of the harder concepts.

8. She gave everything she had, showing the true devotion of her heart.

VI. a. Answers will vary, but need to follow one of the two methods of fixing a run-on sentence. The method used should be indicated by C or D.

   b. Answers will vary, but need to follow one of the two methods of fixing a run-on sentence. The method used should be indicated by C or D.

   c. Answers will vary, but need to follow one of the four methods of fixing a run-on sentence. The method used should be indicated by A, B, C, or D.

Worksheet 29

bridegroom (a man about to be married)

ruthless (showing no pity, merciless, cruel, heartless)

Hosanna (a cry of acclamation or adoration; pray; save us)

magnificent (impressively beautiful, elaborate, noble, extravagant, excellent, splendid, grand)

betray (unfaithful, disloyal; expose, give away)

1. Answers will vary.

2. We should always be ready since we don't know when Jesus is coming back.

3. The servant did not use the money wisely and at least earn interest. He took away the one talent and gave it to the one with three talents. He then threw him out into the night. Answers will vary.

4. Answers will vary.

5. humility and peace

6. once the whole world has heard the truth about Jesus

7. to serve each other with humility and kindness

8. Passover; answers will vary — most likely communion, bread, wine

VI.

1. a. Answers will vary.
   b. Answers will vary.
   c. Answers will vary.

2. a. Answers will vary.
   b. Answers will vary.
   c. Answers will vary.

Worksheet 30

inspired (clever, having influence, suggesting divine influence, outstanding)

courtyard (an enclosure adjacent to a building, an open space surrounded partly or completely by a building)

evidence (a body of facts, testimony, a visible sign, proof, documentation)

riot (public violence, unrestrained revelry, disturbance of the public peace, disorder)

1. a. Answers will vary.
   b. Answers will vary.
   c. Answers will vary.
   d. Answers will vary.

2. Answers will vary and may include: He told them not to be afraid, to trust God, He was going to prepare a place for them, to obey His teaching; He said that He is the vine and they (we) are the branches and to bear fruit, that their tears would turn to joy.

3. with a kiss

4. Simon Peter, Jesus healed him

5. Caiaphas; I am indeed, but I want to add this: there will come a time when you will see the Son of Man seated next to God, coming on the clouds of heaven; he tore his robes in disgust

6. Answers will vary.

7. he thought Jesus was no threat to the Roman government; he feared the crowd would riot and he would lose his job; to show that he took no responsibility for the death of an innocent man

8. they dressed him in a royal purple robe and put a crown of thorns on him; a passer-by; shared them between them by casting lots

9. "Father, forgive them, for they don't understand what they are doing"; "My work is finished! I give my spirit to you, Father"; an earthquake shook the ground and the temple curtain tore from top to bottom; that the barrier between God and people had now been removed

10. Joseph of Arimathea — a rich man and member of the Jewish religious council; a big stone

VI. Answers will vary.

Worksheet 31

dominated (controlled, occupied, elevated, superior position)

vanished (disappeared, ceased to exist)

solemn (serious, grave, somber, grim)

commotion (noisy disturbance, uproar, civil unrest)

1. a. Answers will vary.
   b. Answers will vary.
   c. Answers will vary.
   d. Answers will vary.

2. to anoint Jesus' body with oil; He is alive! He has gone on ahead and will meet you. Go tell Peter and the other disciples what has happened and that he has risen from the dead.

3. they took it away and laid it in some unknown place

4. Thomas refused to believe that Jesus had been resurrected until he touched the holes in Jesus' hands and side.

5. Answers will vary.

6. a spiritual kingdom; in the same way he was taken up to heaven

7. Pentecost; answers will vary

VI. Answers will vary.

Worksheet 32

commissioned (given authority, authorized, commanded, directed to perform a duty, entrusted)

persecute (oppress, harass, abuse, punish, injure, afflict, cause to suffer)

extensively (widely, expansive, broad)

gifted (God-given ability, having a special talent or ability)

1. Answers will vary — the first and last sentence should be underlined.

2. ~~They brought people food.~~

3. a. Barnabas
   b. Aeneas
   c. Tabitha
   d. Peter
   e. Ananias

f. Sappira

g. Philip

4. Answers will vary.

5. Answers will vary.

V. Answers will vary, but must include the elements of a paragraph — a topic sentence, supporting sentences, and a closing sentence. The paragraph should have a central theme or idea.

VI. Answers will vary, but must include the elements of a paragraph — a topic sentence, supporting sentences, and a closing sentence. Each paragraph should have a central theme or idea.

Worksheet 33

nationality (a people group of a specific nation or ethnic group)

ancient (having existed for many years; a time that was long ago)

intervening (the time occurring between events)

acclaimed (applaud, praise, cheer)

magistrates (public officials authorized to administer and enforce the law)

flogged (beat with a whip or stick)

caravan (a group of travelers)

1. Answers will vary — look for imagination, proper sentence structure, and a cohesive story.

2. a. Answers will vary.

   b. Answers will vary.

   c. Answers will vary.

   d. Answers will vary.

   e. Answers will vary.

3. Answers will vary, but should include that the dream was of a sheet of unclean animals

and Peter was told to eat them; God has no special favorites. All people can come to Him whether or not they are Jewish.

4. She forgot to let Peter in.

5. He was blind for a little while; Sergius, the governor, became a follower of Jesus

6. Answers will vary.

7. Answers will vary.

8. Answers will vary, but should show the student has read the passage on page 224.

9. Answers will vary, but should show the student has read the passage on page 225.

VI. Answers will vary — look for imagination, proper sentence structure, a cohesive story, and the proper use of all five elements of a narrative essay.

Worksheet 34

interpreting (explaining the meaning)

pure (spotless, stainless, not mixed with anything else, clean, free from sin or guilt)

mature (having fully developed, adult, ripe, grown up, developed)

splendor (great brightness, impressive beauty, glory, majesty, grandeur)

1. a. imaginative

   b. biography

   c. autobiography

   d. autobiography

2. a. Setting

   b. Characters

   c. Problem

   d. Events

   e. Resolution

3. Answers will vary, but should include the concept that each

part has a purpose and works together with the other parts.

4. Answers will vary, but should include that Paul wrote a letter explaining that Jesus rose from the dead, was seen by many, and Christians will also enjoy an eternal home in heaven.

5. Be ready to meet God without being ashamed of your behavior; be kind, work hard, help the weak, be patient and joyful, pray all the time, thank God, and avoid every kind of evil

6. Answers will vary — see page 230 or Hebrews 11.

7. Answers will vary; those who have been forgiven and whose names are written in the book of life.

V. Answers will vary; parents can find help locating a missionary through their local church or missionary organizations such as Samaritan's Purse or others.

Answers will vary; parents can find help locating persecuted Christians through organizations such as Voice of the Martyrs and others.

VI. Answers will vary.

Answers will vary — look for imagination, proper sentence structure, a cohesive story, and the proper use of all five elements of a narrative essay.

Worksheet 35

1. Answers will vary — look for proper sentence and paragraph structure. The description should make the readers feel as if they can see, hear, taste, or experience the topic.

2. Answers will vary.

3. Answers will vary.

4. Answers will vary.

5. Answers will vary.

6. Answers will vary and will be different depending on whether the student is a boy or a girl.

7. Answers will vary.

8. a. **Rosh Hashanah** (September–October; Jewish New Year)

   b. **Yom Kippur** (September–October; Day of Atonement, when Jewish people fast and pray)

   c. **Succoth** (September–October; celebration of the grape and olive harvest and the end of the farming year. People camped in huts or booths for Succoth, which mean the "Feast of Booths.")

   d. **Hanukkah** (December; the Feast of Lights celebrates the rededication of the temple in Jerusalem by Judas Maccabeus around 164 B.C. Candles are lit on each of the eight days of the festival.)

   e. **Purim** (February–March; celebration of how Queen Esther saved the Jews from their enemies)

   f. **The Passover** (March–April; commemoration of the Exodus from Egypt. The angel of death killed every first-born Egyptian, but "passed over" the Israelites.)

   g. **Shavuot** (May–June; remembers the day that Moses received the Ten Commandments. It is also known as the Feast of Weeks.)

9. Answers will vary.

10. Answers will vary.

11. Answers will vary.

12. Bethlehem; Nazareth

13. a. The Sea of Galilee (It is a large freshwater lake, about 12 miles long and 7 miles wide.)

    b. It is the biggest and longest river in Israel. It rises in the north of the country and flows southward, through the Sea of Galilee to the Dead Sea.

    c. It is a salt lake that lies about 1,300 feet below sea level, making it the lowest place on earth. The water is so salty that no fish can live there, which is how the lake got its name.

14. It is a rocky desert area that lies west of the river Jordan. People couldn't grow crops or live there, so in biblical times it was a lonely and desolate place.

Worksheet 36

1. a. **Ur:** (Abraham lived there before God commanded him to travel to Canaaan.)

   b. **Egypt:** (Joseph was sold into slavery there and became one of the pharaoh's ministers. His family's descendants lived there for many years until the Egyptians treated them as slaves and Moses led them out in the "exodus.")

   c. **Sinai:** (The Israelites spent 40 years wandering the desert there.)

   d. **Babylon:** (A large number of Israelites were taken there when the Babylonians seized Jerusalem and destroyed the temple.)

   e. **Damascus:** (Paul was traveling there when he was converted to Christianity.)

   f. **Rome:** (Peter and Paul were put to death there.)

   g. **Corinth, Thessalonica and Philippi:** (Paul traveled here on two of his missionary journeys and founded important early churches.)

   h. **Athens:** (Paul visited Athens on his second journey and disputed with the local philosophers.)

   i. **Ephesus** (Paul visited Ephesus on two of his missionary journeys and helped establish a church there. His preaching upset the followers of Diana, and eventually caused a riot.)

2. Adam, Eve, Noah, Abraham, Sarah, Isaac, Esau, Jacob, Joseph (son of Jacob),

   Moses, Aaron, Joshua, Deborah, Gideon, Samson, Ruth,

   Hannah, Samuel, Saul, David, Solomon, Elijah, Elisha,

   Ezra, Nehemiah, Esther, Job, Isaiah, Jeremiah, Ezekiel, Daniel,

   Jesus, Mary (mother of Jesus), Joseph (husband of Mary), John the Baptist,

   Peter, James (son of Zebedee), John (the apostle), Matthew, Thomas, Judas Iscariot,

   James (brother of Jesus), Pontius Pilate, Zacchaeus,

   Mark, Paul, Timothy, Luke

Quiz 1

1. **salvation** (being saved from the power and penalty of sin)

   famine (a shortage of food in a particular region)

   exodus (a departure of a large number or people)

   prophet (one instructed by God to speak in His name)

2. a. **The Law:** These books describe the origin of the Jewish people and culture.

   b. **History:** These books describe the historical accounts of the Israelites.

   c. **Poetry:** These books deal with important questions of life.

   d. **Prophecy:** In these books, prophets predicted future events, especially about the coming Messiah.

3. a. The ⓑible is a collection of many books of different kinds of writing.

   b. The ⓑible has one central message: ⓖod's salvation of His people.

4. a. God appeared to Abraham in a vision.

   b. Abraham trembled before God.

5. a. I ⓦill give this land to you and your many descendants.

   b. Jacob ⓦas amazed that God had spoken to him.

6. communion

7. a. Answers will vary.

   b. Answers will vary.

8. a. Thou shalt love the Lord thy God with all thy heart, and with all thy soul, and with all thy mind.

   b. Thou shalt love thy neighbor as thyself.

9. a. Moses, you will soon die.

   b. Slowly he climbed Mount Nebo.

10. a. Gideon

    b. Boaz

11. a. Ruth stayed by Naomi's side.

    b. Ruth set the grain down.

Quiz 2

1. **anoint** (to apply oil to set them apart for sacred use)

   gratitude (thankful, grateful, appreciation)

   prophesied (predict that something will happen in the future, foretell)

   exile (a person forced to leave his or her country)

2. a. Samuel, heard by God

   b. Saul, David, Solomon

3. Answers will vary, but in most cases having a king was not good and did not help the people serve God better.

4. a. That's

   b. We're

5. a. His weapons

   b. God

   c. Jerusalem

6. a. At Bethel the resident prophets said to Elisha, "Do you realize that God is going to take Elijah away from you soon?"

   b. As Elisha saw it, he cried out, "My Father! The chariots and horsemen of Israel!"

7. a. They turned his heart away from God.

   b. Jezebel

   c. Elisha

8. Answers will vary.

9. Answers will vary. See page 99.

10. Answers will vary.

11. a collection of wise sayings about the best way to live

12. a God-centered life

13. the destruction of Israel by the Assyrians

14. a. lives

    b. loaves

Quiz 3

1. **gospel** (good news)

   Gentile (a person who is not Jewish, a heathen or pagan, a nonbeliever)

   parable (a short story intended to teach a moral or spiritual truth)

   eternal (forever, undying, infinite)

2. Answers will vary, but may include: they were fitter and healthier than the Israelites who had eaten the royal food.)

3. a. **fry:** (Answers will vary — check for spelling.)

   b. **lonely:** (Answers will vary — check for spelling.)

   c. **costly:** (Answers will vary

d. **amplify**: (Answers will vary — check for spelling.)

e. **crunchy**: (Answers will vary — check for spelling.)

4. a. **Can**: (able to; metal container usually shaped like a cylinder)

 b. **Fall**: (to drop down quickly; a season, autumn)

5. We do not know, but it is often assumed three because there were three gifts.

6. gold, frankincense, myrrh

7. John the Baptist; the Holy Spirit came upon Jesus like a dove and a voice cried out from heaven, "This is my own dear Son and I am very pleased with him."

8. the Old Testament

9. turning water into wine at a wedding at Cana in Galilee

10. one

11. picked corn and ate it, healed people

12. Answers will vary — see page 166 of text.

13. His own body

14. 12 baskets

15. a. Do not tell anyone about the transfiguration of Jesus.)

 b. A priest came by and acted like he did not see anything.

16. Answers will vary — see page 180 of text.

Quiz 4

1. **resurrection** (rising from the dead, a dead person coming back to life)

 inspired (clever, having influence, suggesting divine influence, outstanding)

 persecute (oppress, harass, abuse, punish, injure, afflict, cause to suffer)

 ancient (having existed for many years; a time that was long ago)

2. Answers will vary — see Worksheet 28.

3. humility and peace

4. once the whole world has heard the truth about Jesus

5. Simon Peter; Jesus healed him

6. "Father, forgive them, for they don't understand what they are doing"; "My work is finished! I give my spirit to you, Father"; an earthquake shook the ground and the temple curtain tore from top to bottom; that the barrier between God and people had now been removed.

7. a spiritual kingdom; in the same way he was taken up to heaven

8. a. Barnabas

 b. Aeneas

 c. Tabitha

 d. Peter

 e. Ananias

 f. Sappira

 g. Philip

9. She forgot to let Peter in.

10. a. setting

 b. characters

 c. problem

 d. events

 e. resolution

11. Answers will vary, but should include the concept that each part has a purpose and works together with the other parts.

12. be ready to meet God without being ashamed of your behavior, be kind, work hard, help the weak, be patient and joyful, pray all the time, thank God, and avoid every kind of evil

Test Your Knowledge 1

Old Testament

1. Adam and Eve
2. Abraham
3. Lot's wife
4. Joseph
5. Moses
6. Rahab
7. Naomi
8. Eli
9. Jonathan
10. Solomon
11. Elisha
12. Joash
13. Job
14. Daniel

New Testament

1. Zechariah
2. Gold, frankincense, and myrrh
3. Nazareth
4. Cana
5. thirty pieces of silver
6. fisherman
7. Damascus
8. sycamore
9. rock
10. Herodias
11. Nicodemus
12. Jesus of Nazareth, King of the Jews
13. Gaza
14. twelve
15. Pentecost
16. Malta

Test Your Knowledge 2

General

1. Mount Horeb
2. Mount Carmel
3. trumpets
4. oil
5. Bethlehem
6. Damascus
7. Ephesus
8. Jonah
9. good news
10. sixty-six
11. Nero

The Natural World

1. dove
2. donkey
3. snake
4. cock
5. olive tree
6. pigeon
7. ravens
8. Ararat
9. Lake of Gennesaret (Sea of Galilee)
10. Jorden
11. locusts

Levels 1-5
MATH LESSONS FOR A LIVING EDUCATION

Angela O'Dell

A CHARLOTTE MASON FLAVOR TO MATH FOR TODAY'S STUDENT
- Story Based
- Short Lessons
- Hands-on Activities
- Learning Review

MASTERBOOKS
—CURRICULUM—

ATTRACTIVE FULL-COLOR LESSONS

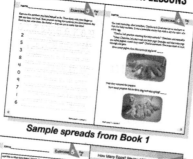

Sample spreads from Book 1

AVAILABLE AT
MASTERBOOKS.COM
& OTHER PLACES WHERE
FINE BOOKS ARE SOLD.

Level 1, Grade 1
Learning numbers
100, circles and pa
counting and addit
days of the week, a
telling time.
Downloadable answe
978-0-89051-923-3

Level 2, Grade 2
Subtraction, writin
numbers to 100,
introducing word p
and measurement,
dollars and cents.
Downloadable answe
978-0-89051-924-0

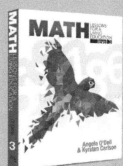

Level 3, Grade 3
Column addition,
introducing multipl
and division, and F
numerals.
Removable answer ke
back of book
978-0-89051-925-7

Level 4, Grade 4
New fraction conce
metric units of
measurement, bas
geometry, and ave
Removable solutions
in back of book
978-0-89051-926-4

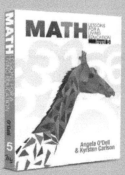

Level 5, Grade 5
Factoring, imprope
fractions, common
uncommon denom
and multiplying de
Removable solutions
in back of book
978-0-89051-927-1

ELEMENTARY GEOGRAPHY & CULTURES

3RD–6TH GRADE / 1 YEAR

Explore continents, countries, and cultures around the globe! Discover biomes, history, government systems, heritage sites, recipes, wide-ranging facts and details as well as Christian connections everywhere you go with these photo-rich resources! Enjoy this 3-book package as elementary curriculum and as valued reference tools.

CHILDREN'S ATLAS OF GOD'S WORLD 978-0-89051-706-2
PASSPORT TO THE WORLD 978-0-89051-595-2
TEACHER GUIDE 978-0-89051-996-7
3 BOOK SET 978-0-89051-814-4

MASTERBOOKS
— CURRICULUM —

AVAILABLE AT
MASTERBOOKS.COM
& OTHER PLACES WHERE FINE BOOKS ARE SOLD.

Daily Lesson Plans

WE'VE DONE THE WORK FOR YO

PERFORATED & 3-HOLE PUNCHE
FLEXIBLE 180-DAY SCHEDULE
DAILY LIST OF ACTIVITIES
RECORD KEEPING

"THE TEACHER GUIDE MAKES T
SO MUCH EASIER AND TAKE
GUESS WORK OUT OF IT FO

★★★★

HOMESCHOO

Master Books® Homeschool Curricu

Faith-Building Books & Resources
Parent-Friendly Lesson Plans
Biblically-Based Worldview
Affordably Priced

**Master Books® is the leading publisher of books and resource
based upon a Biblical worldview that points to God as our Cr**
Now the books you love, from the authors you trust like Ken Ham, Michael Farris,
Tommy Mitchell, and many more are available as a homeschool curriculum.

MASTERBOOKS
Where Faith Grow